# HEAVENLY DISCOURSE

*by*

CHARLES ERSKINE SCOTT WOOD

*With drawings by* ART YOUNG
*& frontispiece by* HUGO GELLERT

NEW YORK                    MCMXXVIII

MACY-MASIUS : THE VANGUARD PRESS

THIS LIBRARY EDITION OF
HEAVENLY DISCOURSE
PUBLISHED AUGUST, 1928
SECOND PRINTING, OCTOBER, 1928

# HEAVENLY
# DISCOURSE

# FOREWORD

THE *Heavenly Discourse* of C. E. S. Wood is a contribution of permanent importance to American literature. The satires are, in their wit and truth and imagination, the expression of a large and noble mind; and they establish for their author an honorable place in the great tradition of humanistic satire with which the names of Aristophanes, Lucian, Rabelais, Swift, Mark Twain, Anatole France and Bernard Shaw are associated.

To mock at the follies of one's day is not a task for little minds; their littleness—their want of generosity and taste and sense—is too easily revealed. To succeed in this province of literature requires a lofty and sensitive spirit. And communion with such a spirit enriches and uplifts our own minds, and makes us braver to bear the struggle of the day.

*Heavenly Discourse* was among the bright meteors that flamed through the pages of the old *Masses*, of which I had the honor to be an editor. I used to read proof on each Discourse and see it through the press in magazine form; and it gives me great pleasure to have something to do with their appearance as a book. In saying this, I speak for all the editors of the old *Masses*; and in praising them, I know that I speak for all its readers.

April, 1927.                                    FLOYD DELL

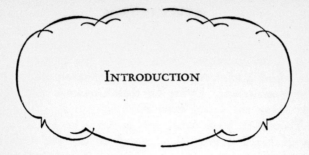

# INTRODUCTION

MOST of these satires were written for the *Masses* but only a few were published.

That brilliant journal fell, a sacrifice to the "War to end War" and for "Freedom and Democracy."

The unpublished bits were returned to me—I use that sacred word timidly, yet I like to think that during the World War for the weaker peoples I also did my bit. Max Eastman and others urged that I bring them out as a book, and Art Young desired to renew his acquaintance by contributing a few sketches—but, until now, no publisher was interested. One objection was that "their day had passed"—they were mostly about the war and were not "timely".

I should be glad to think so. The war for world salvation has passed, but not *war*. We are still Christians. Our capitalistic plutocrats thirst to exploit the world. The planet is their orange. The city of George Washington is blossoming into quite a nice little seat of empire and centralized bureaucracy. The people have a passion to "let Uncle Sam do it". The federal courts are police courts. An entire system with an army of officials has risen on the income tax; another on prohibition. The freedom of the common man, more vital to progress than income or alcohol, has vanished. The next war will be put over more easily. It will be a combat between two empires as to which shall possess the planet—but who cares? In the Eternal City of the Church an imitation Caesar receives the salutation of the young gladiators, *Ave Caesar, Imperator; nos morituri te salutamus.* Dying for their Caesars is about the best thing the young men do.

Though in book form, this is not a book. It is a lot of beads strung on a thread or say the twisted threads of freedom of mind, body and soul and war; which in the end destroys the strongest. I have added a few up-to-date ones, but the book remains a disconnected collection of essays. Against such as were published there was at that time objection from some quarters—"blasphemous", "irreverent". Fortunately "blasphemy" is not yet in the state or federal constitutions, battered and shattered though they be by the judicial Galahads who, during the war for freedom, etc., etc., etc., thought the Holy Grail was hidden somewhere in France, England, or the United States, but certainly not in Germany or Russia. Blasphemy is a matter of religious opinion, just as democracy and freedom are questions of political opinion, and opinion—religious or political—is not yet a crime. I am eager to have the "irreverence" shown me. Reverence is not due to crowns or halos—heavenly or earthly—but to purity of spirit, greatness of soul, and goodness of deed. Any god fit to be a god must be at least as broad, tolerant, and kind as many men are. I fancy such a god would only smile at the irreverences of Billy Sunday, the vaudeville of certain "ministers of the Gospel" and the bloodthirstiness of his lambs in wolves' clothing.

Familiarity with Jesus there is, yes. Much more than his followers show, but he was familiar with common men—and if his "followers" will in daily act and deed, in market and in politics, make a living truth of the brotherhood of man, I will show them reverence, as in these essays I show Jesus all reverence. There would be no more war if the Golden Rule were believed and lived.

Wars come from greed and hate,—great wealth concentrated in a few by privileges and monopolies—investments abroad of this superabundant wealth—imperialism—and the fight of world-dogs for the world-bone. *Pax vobiscum.*

CHARLES ERSKINE SCOTT WOOD

# CONTENTS

# ILLUSTRATIONS

# HEAVENLY
# DISCOURSE

DRAMATIS PERSONAE

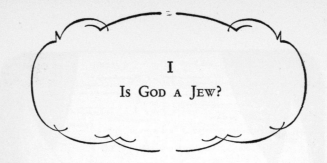

# I

## Is God a Jew?

(GOD *is at the wheel of the Universe, turning the stars.* JESUS *enters.*)

JESUS: Father, are we Jews?
GOD: What?
JESUS: Are we Jews?
GOD: Where is Peter?
JESUS: At the gate.
GOD: Tell him to come take the wheel.
JESUS: Shall he lock the gate?
GOD: No. Leave it open. Maybe some interesting person will stray in.

(*Jesus goes out and presently returns with* ST. PETER. GOD *turns over the wheel to* ST. PETER, *and beckons* JESUS *to follow him. They go apart.*)
Now, my son, what did you say?

JESUS: Are we Jews?
GOD (*looking cautiously around*): We are. You and I and your mother are the only pure-blooded Jews left.
JESUS: But I thought Jews——
GOD: Well, they are——
JESUS: But if you and I and mother are good enough for Christians——
GOD: Yes, I know. Talk to your Christians.
JESUS: Isn't Peter, over there, a Jew?

GOD: Of course. And Matthew and Mark and Luke and John and Paul—all your disciples. Don't argue with me, my son—convert your Christians to Christianity.

JESUS: But, Father, if the Christians take you and me and mother and the prophets and the apostles, all their religion, their ten commandments, their morals and their Bible from the Jews, what's the matter with the Jews?

GOD: The Jews reject you.

JESUS: So do the Christians.

GOD: The Jews crucified you.

JESUS: So do the Christians. But Romans crucified me and now Rome is the cornerstone.

GOD: Talk to your Christians.

JESUS: Father, you know they reject me.

GOD: The Jews have been poor and down-trodden. In a new freedom and sudden riches some of them are pushing and crowding, vulgar.

JESUS: So are some Christians, and there are Jews of great culture—refinement. Philosophers, scientists, artists, idealists.

GOD: Yes. But they are Jews. Who told you we were Jews?

JESUS: The Devil.

GOD: The Devil? Is he back?

JESUS: Yes, but not to stay. He says you couldn't hire him to stay. He wants a contract to light and move the stars. He says he can generate enough power in hell to run the universe.

GOD: By myself, he's a smart devil——

JESUS: He says if you will give him a good contract he will join the Christian churches; says he has lots of friends in all of them.

GOD: By myself, he is a smart devil. Go on.

JESUS: He will pray once a week, like the rest, and if you will allow him for overtime, he will pray on week days.

GOD: Clever devil! He knows I am simply swamped with prayers.

JESUS: Why do you not forgive Satan, Father?

GOD: Forgive? I have nothing to forgive. You must not be deceived by man's idea of me as a god of vengeance. I am without mercy, but also without hate.

JESUS: O, Father, how can man live without mercy?

GOD: Why should he live? But about Satan——

JESUS: Well, he said you and he ought to work together because you were both Jews, but I said we were not Jews. Then he laughed and said, "Go ask your father."

GOD: Yes, my son, you and I are Jews. I was born a Jew.

JESUS: Were you born, Father?

GOD: Certainly. Every god is born of man. The Jews conceived me. I was conceived and born a Jew.

JESUS: When was that, Father?

GOD: Oh, a long time ago; before you were born.

JESUS: Well, how did it happen that you became a Christian?

GOD: O, I never did. No. Not as bad as that. Your Christians kidnapped me. There should be two words, my son: *Christ*-ian, for those who actually live your teachings; and Christian for the prayer-snivelling hypocrites.

JESUS: Kidnapped you?

GOD: Yes; from the Jews. On your account.

JESUS: My account?

GOD: About a hundred years or so after you were

first crucified by the Law and Order Committee of Jerusalem, the common people went crazy over you, because you taught equality, brotherhood and peace, here and hereafter, and resurrection after death. The resurrection idea caught them.

JESUS: I never promised resurrection of the body; but only of the spirit.

GOD: Well, your followers gave out that idea, and the idea of peace and love, and you became the hope of the world, so your mother and I were adopted because we were your parents. It's all right. It was good business.

JESUS: I am glad they did not break up the family.

GOD: Paul ruined you. He organized you into an institution and later you were hitched to the Roman Empire, and so captured Christendom. Christendom?

JESUS: Why do you laugh, Father?

GOD: O, it is so amusing. You see it really means Christ's kingdom. Yours, my son, the Prince of Peace, of love, of universal brotherhood. No wars.

JESUS: To me it is sad.

GOD: Dear, beloved son, you should see the humor of it—but, no, you were always the child of sorrow. Well, well. Now, thanks to Paul and the Roman Empire, you are a great, powerful, political, financial, worldly institution, or rather a bunch of them. Your first church wasn't Christian enough to stay together.

JESUS: Oh, see the shooting-stars!

GOD: Collision. That's what comes of leaving Peter at the wheel.

(GOD *hurries back to his post.*)

JESUS: So I am a Jew. I am glad of it. I am glad to be kin to the old prophets and poets, who spoke the great ideals. We have been persecuted and oppressed,

GOD AT THE WHEEL

but always we have kept love of beauty, imagination, and our ideals. Reject me? No. They may reject the foolish superstitions a childish and credulous age has woven around me, but me, the great Jew who preached love, tolerance, and peace they will not reject.

(JESUS *goes slowly out.*)

## II

### MARRIAGE

(GOD *and* JESUS *are strolling through the universe, stepping from star to star.*)

JESUS: Father, how small the earth is in the infinity of space, among stars, bewildering in magnitude.

GOD: Yes. A speck. Why are you so fond of it?

JESUS: I don't know. Because they crucified me, I guess.

GOD: Well, yes, I can understand that.

JESUS: We love where we forgive, and we never forget where we have suffered.

GOD: No, I suppose not. I never suffered.

JESUS: Didn't you suffer when Aaron set up the golden calf?

GOD: No. I made him suffer.

JESUS: Father, am I the only son you ever had?

GOD: No, my son. I have had many sons, but you are the only son I ever had by a Jewess.

JESUS: Father, were you and mother ever married?

GOD: Ever what?

JESUS: Married. Holy matrimony. Holy wedlock.

GOD: Holy smoke! what are you talking about?

JESUS: On earth when a man and a woman love and want to unite their lives, they have first to get leave or license from somebody—then they have to stand before a priest or some other man and say something, and he tells them all right they may love. They are married. But when you are married, it is for forever and you can never go apart, even though you grow out of love and are very unhappy.

GOD: My son, your earth-visits are beginning to affect your mind.

JESUS: I don't say this. But they say it is your law.

GOD: Who says so?

JESUS: The priests and the county clerk.

GOD: When you want to know my law come to me —or look around you. You don't see or hear this foolishness anywhere else, do you?

JESUS: No, only where there are men and priests.

GOD: My laws are universal. Your mother and I loved each other and you were born as flowers are born.

JESUS: Then I am a bastard?

GOD: What do you mean?

JESUS: On earth, if the father and mother are not married, the child is a bastard. And I was born on earth.

GOD: You don't seem to be able to get away from that perfectly absurd earth.

JESUS: No, it's not that, but now in the midst of this war to end war, they want to get more babies for soldiers in the next war and there will be a lot of poor little innocent bastards. The Church——

GOD: Don't mention it. We have nothing to do with it.

JESUS: And the State——

GOD: What's that?

JESUS: The rich few who govern the people.

GOD: O, gods?

JESUS: Yes, in a way. The Church and the State, in order to have more men for more wars, are urging a lot of young men and women to take out permission papers for leave to love and have babies.

GOD: That's marriage?

JESUS: Yes.

GOD: Holy matrimony?

JESUS: Yes.

GOD: What makes it holy?

JESUS: The love of the pair for each other.

GOD: What has the Church or the State to do with that?

JESUS: Nothing. But as I was saying, the Church and the State urged the young people to get babies; certificates, I mean, so that they could get more babies for more wars.

GOD: Couldn't they get any babies without this certificate?

JESUS: Certainly, and that's the trouble. A lot of young people are doing it, but the children will be bastards.

GOD: Won't they be just as good babies?

JESUS: Yes.

GOD: Did the babies insist on certificates?

JESUS: No.

GOD: Won't they make just as good soldiers and mothers of soldiers? The boys can be killed just the same?

JESUS: O, yes.

GOD: Then what's the trouble?

JESUS: I don't know. Only, if the parents are not legally married, the babies are bastards.

GOD: So they punish the babies? Is it marked on them?

JESUS: No.

GOD: Does it hurt their health?

JESUS: No, Father, but Christians look down on them. They say such births are not lawful.

GOD: Christians look down on most everything that is loving and sensible.  Has this loving and pairing without permission been going on very long?

JESUS: Ever since creation.

GOD: My! My! How awful!

JESUS: Father, you are mocking.

GOD: I have to—in order not to send an affliction on your stupid, silly pismires and blot them out. But they will do that themselves. Why not kill the unlawfuls as soon as born? Why let them be born?

JESUS: O, the State and the Church can use them; but the idea is this: the parents are rebels, in a way. They didn't have leave from Church and State to get these babies.

GOD: Well, I'll be—no, of course, I couldn't be. Listen. Won't these babies grow up to be men and women?

JESUS: Yes. But the Church and the State will call them bastards. They'll be forever disgraced.

GOD: Who? The Church and the State?

JESUS: No, the babies.

GOD: Are you disgraced?

JESUS: No, Father. I am your beloved son.

GOD: My beloved son. Who was never smirched by Church or State. Leave to love. Let us go home. Your talk has made me just a little tired. I can endure anything but stupidity. My law is—The stupid shall pass away.

# III

## GOD RECEIVES A DELEGATION

(*The Plane of Peace.* GOD *is listening to the music of the spheres—slowly moving his head in harmony with the rhythm.*)

(HERMES *comes in.*)

HERMES: Omnipotence and Omniscience, there is a delegation from the earth desires to see you.

GOD: From where?

HERMES: Earth.

GOD: What is that? Where is it?

HERMES: Jesus' earth.

GOD: O, yes. Patience. Patience. It too will end. Tell them to come in.

(*A mob of tourist angels comes in.*)

SPOKESMAN: We have just arrived from earth.

GOD: You are very welcome. The fundamentalists will find harps and halos on the fifty-seventh plane below this. I want to caution the bankers and business men that it is useless to dig up the golden pavement. It is valueless here. We have had a great deal of trouble about that from earthly visitors. Tubal-Cain will show the machinery to those interested. The scientists will find their comrades in the Crystal Chamber with Krishna who will explain to them all they wish to know. The artists and poets may remain here with me. Thank you.

PROF. IRVING FISHER: I am a Prohibitionist. I——

GOD: You are in the wrong place. Sorry. Show him out, Hermes.

IRVING FISHER: But I invented the idea that the more prohibition there is the more liberty you have.

MARK TWAIN: I also am a humorist.

GOD: Remain, Samuel. You will find many friends—Aristophanes, Rabelais, Cervantes, Shakespeare, Dickens. I do not know what heaven would do without the humorists and poets. My beloved son, Jesus, the great poet.

CARRIE NATION: I am a reformer.

GOD: A what?

CARRIE NATION: A reformer. I make people better.

GOD: How?

CARRIE NATION: By my hatchet.

GOD: O! By force? By jail and punishment. It never has been done. You don't belong here. It is another of Peter's mistakes. I must abolish that gate of his. It is too much like censorship—too much like privilege and monopoly. Too much like judging your fellows. It is not freedom, and freedom is heaven's first law. I think with Peter's gate gone and absolute freedom established, heaven will become more interesting, more life-like. However, you may go with the fundamentalists and you will have fifty-six planes of growth before you reach here. Show them out, Hermes.

(HERMES *gently drives out all but the scientists, artists, poets, and* MARK TWAIN.)

Come, we are now all kindred spirits. Scientists are poets also. Let us go to the Crystal Chamber.

MARK TWAIN: (*Aside*) He's not half bad. Not at all as represented.

(*All go out.*)

# IV
## FREEDOM

(GOD *is walking, alone, on the Crystal Battlements.*
MARK TWAIN *joins him.*)

MARK TWAIN: Omniscience, I have a curiosity to
know your thoughts.

GOD: Curiosity is godly, Samuel. It is mental thirst.
I was thinking how wise I was to establish certain general principles in the beginning and to leave them to
operate in freedom, in utter freedom, through eternity,
producing continual growth where accepted and destruction where opposed. How much better than to
attempt to meet each problem with some special plan
devised for the occasion, only to find later that it must
be altered and so move from blunder to blunder as your
people in the Us land do.

MARK TWAIN: Us-land?

GOD: Isn't it Us? What was your country on earth?

MARK TWAIN: United States of America.

GOD: That's it—U.S. They think they are the whole
thing so I confused it with "Us." Well, that's the
trouble with your country. They are always patching,
always trying to dodge the great cosmic principles; to
dodge freedom. Every blessing has its price and they are
never willing to take a chance with liberty and pay the
price.

If there be trouble because of the banking and money monopoly, instead of free banking they put on a patch. If there be trouble because of planet monopoly—water, land, minerals, timber, etc., instead of allowing the planet to be free to beneficial users, they put on patch after patch. If there be trouble about transportation, telegraph and telephone, instead of declaring they are tools of the people, they put on a patch. If there be drunkenness, instead of education and regulation they apply a patch. And as for trade, instead of trade being free, it is patched hopelessly. Always patching, patching—never going to the root.

MARK TWAIN: Yes, the poor old U.S. is a crazy-quilt. But, Omniscience, if you saw the people elected to govern and the people who elect them, you would be surprised that things are not worse;—sand-fleas, sand-fleas.

GOD: I thought they had schools.

MARK TWAIN: Schools. Teachers aren't allowed to teach anything real or true or living. They cannot teach that which is most important of all—how to think; how to examine; how to use intellect and reason rather than be trapped by fool words, words, words.

Pupils are brought up to a superstitious reverence of the dead past. They are taught a flag idolatry that blinds the youth to the fact that today the flag at home stands for suppression of free speech, free press, free theatre, personal freedom, and abroad, stands for conquest and rule and looting of weaker peoples. The flag —the piece of bunting—is made holier than that resistance to oppression which gave it birth. Let any one advocate evolution, change, progress, freedom—and a mob is loosed against him—a mob taught intolerance in the schools; taught that the individual can be ordered, commanded, bullied, crushed; falsely taught that the flag still stands for democracy and freedom, and that patriotism and loyalty mean devotion to a free country of noble ideals. As a matter of fact, the country is owned by a few, very few, and the ideals are the piratical ideals of an imperialistic oligarchy—suppression of slaves at home, conquest and exploitation of new territory and new slaves abroad.

GOD: Is there no freedom in your country, Samuel?

MARK TWAIN: Freedom. A general of the army— Fries by name—Chief of the Poison Gas Division— tried to have a school teacher removed because he had written for a leading magazine a prize essay explaining Socialism.

GOD: O! But you don't expect brains among the military?

MARK TWAIN: No. I suppose the best we can expect is Lamb Fries. But this arrogant, stupid intolerance is what the holy war for democracy did to democracy. Now they are yelling their heads off for another war. Bigger armies—bigger navies—big cruisers, small cruisers, aircraft, submarines. Conquer Mexico, conquer the world. Why, it's war—war—war in the heavens above, the earth beneath, and the waters under the earth.

GOD: You know your Bible, Samuel.

MARK TWAIN: I do, but they don't. Not Jesus' end of it. What makes me mad is their stupidity. There couldn't be any war if the people refused to fight and wouldn't pay war taxes. But the fools just love to work for their masters and are dippy to die for them.

GOD: What's "dippy," Samuel?

MARK TWAIN: Crazy—silly—eager.

GOD: Second, Samuel, I think I ought to destroy the earth.

MARK TWAIN: Don't trouble yourself. Leave it to man.

GOD: I wouldn't destroy anything for being wicked. Wickedness is a fashion. It changes. But stupidity never does. Man is just stupidly stupid.

MARK TWAIN: Didn't you destroy San Francisco because is was so wicked?

GOD: O yes, of course.

MARK TWAIN: Then why did you destroy all the churches and the Y. M. C. A. and leave standing the dance halls of the Barbary Coast and the gambling saloons of Montgomery Street?

GOD: I was confused that day, Samuel. Don't mention it to anyone, but I thought the churches were worse than the brothels. I didn't see my son Jesus near the churches but I saw him with the dancers. Have you met any of my sons?

MARK TWAIN: Not yet, Lord. I am from the earth.

GOD: Isn't Jesus known there?

MARK TWAIN: No, Lord. Only a speaking acquaintance.

(GABRIEL *appears*.)

GOD: Gabriel, will you please blow the Family Assembly?

(GABRIEL *goes out. The playing of a horn is heard*.)

MARK TWAIN: Why pick on San Francisco? Why not Paris or London?

GOD: Samuel, I burned Chicago and San Francisco because they were bad. And I burned Baltimore because it was good. I struck dead Ananias and Sapphira, his wife, for lying, and for lying I rewarded Jacob and Rebecca, his mother. I struck dead Percy Stickney Grant for being a modernist and I struck William Jennings Bryan dead for being a fundamentalist. I am the most erratic assassin and arsonist in all history.

MARK TWAIN: You are a humorist.

GOD: That is why you are here, Samuel. Listen. When a man says "God" wants the world purified, "God" wants a theatre so clean it will smell like a hospital, "God" wants no more drinking or dancing or merry-making, he lies. What he really means is that his own impure, tyrannical, bigoted, narrow, intolerant, petty soul wants the whole world to be like him. Man looks into a dim mirror and sees his god. I want nothing so much as freedom, freedom, always freedom—body, soul, and mind free, then let us see what will come of it.

MARK TWAIN: Surely something great.

GOD: Yes, Samuel. If there be greatness in man. Surely greater than the prison bars or the slave-driver's whip can ever bring forth.

(JESUS, GAUTAMA, LAO-TZE, CONFUCIUS, *and* SOCRATES *come in.*)

These, Samuel, are some of my sons.

MARK TWAIN: The Chinamen, too? And the Hindu?

GOD: O, yes. Among the greatest. Lao-tze taught that the path to heaven was by treading underfoot the fierce ambition to enslave and destroy others. Confucius taught that we must not do to others what we would not wish done to ourselves. Gautama taught peace, not to kill, and to return good for evil, saying, "If thine enemy come to thy door give him shelter, give him food, for the tree refuses not its shade to the ax-man at its root," and Socrates taught that love is the builder, hate the destroyer. He said the good man must always be good. If he returns evil for evil he is no longer good. So he must return good for evil.

These sons of mine were five hundred years before their brother Jesus, my beloved son.

MARK TWAIN: I am fortunate to have seen all the sons of God.

GOD: Not all. I have many sons. Samuel and I were discussing a matter of interest to the earth-born. Shall I destroy the earth now or leave it to its own destruction?

JESUS: Father, you have been out of patience with the earth so often.

GOD: No, only with man.

JESUS: But each time I have had to remind you that I have your promise that I and my brothers may have a million years of trial for our teachings.

GOD: Jesus, you are such an optimist.

JESUS: But, Father, through you the earth has produced us.

GOD: And look what it did to you. Look at it now. A perfect mess of hate, greed, and war—and sowing seed for more war. No freedom anywhere.

JESUS: But you promised.

GOD: O, well. What's a million years? The ants or the monkeys will own the earth then. There is no hope but freedom and man cannot comprehend it.

JESUS: There is no hope but brotherly love.

GOD: And man cannot comprehend it.

SOCRATES: There is no hope but justice.

GOD: And man cannot comprehend it.

GAUTAMA: There is no hope but the spirit which devoutly contemplates peace.

GOD: And man cannot comprehend it.

LAO-TZE: There is no hope from the body but only from the soul.

GOD: And man cannot comprehend it.

CONFUCIUS: There is no hope but men do as they would be done by.

MARK TWAIN: And man cannot comprehend it.

GOD: Love, not hate—soul, not material things—truth, not falsity. Freedom in all things—these could be man's salvation through a glorious peace in which every moment sings as it goes, but man cannot comprehend it. Let us each go apart and meditate on the infinities of the universe, forgetting the earth.

(*All go out.*)

## V

## THE MONKEYS COMPLAIN

(God *is lying on the bank of the River of Life, reading The Book of Life.*)

(St. Peter *comes in.*)

GOD: Well, Peter, what now? It does seem as if I never take a little rest but you butt in.

ST. PETER: It's an awful job, Lord—janitor to heaven.

GOD: Well, what is it now?

ST. PETER: A delegation from the Monkey Heaven wants to see you.

GOD: Not William Sunday?

ST. PETER: No—the Monkey Heaven.

GOD: Didn't he go to the Monkey Heaven?

ST. PETER: No, the African Medicine Man's Heaven.

GOD: Very well. Bring them here.

(St. Peter *goes out.*)

I wonder what's up now. The monkeys have been a very fine lot, giving no trouble.

(St. Peter *returns with a gorilla, a chimpanzee, and an orang-outang.*)

ST. PETER: Here they are, Lord.

GOD: What is it, my good people?

THE GORILLA: God, shake hands with Jim, one of our leading chimpanzees; Tango, same among orang-outangs; and my name is George—Gorilla family, **very** old and honorable.

GOD: Glad to make your acquaintance. Now what is it?

GEORGE: No, no. Excuse me. The "What-is-it" was a fake by Barnum. He was a man, an idiot.

GOD: If he was a man, of course he was an idiot. I mean what do you want?

GEORGE: Jim, you tell him.

JIM: You see, it's like this. There is a trial going on down earth way, at Dayton, Tennessee, between a set who say man is a monkey, or was a monkey, or will be a monkey, or is descended from a monkey, or is cousin to a monkey, or something like that; and a set who say he isn't, but he is now just exactly as you made him at the start, only worse.

GOD: As I made him——

(GOD *groans.*)

JIM: Eh?

GOD: Nothing. Go **on.**

(GOD *groans.*)

JIM: Aren't you well?

GOD: Only nausea. I get that way when I talk of man. Go on.

JIM: It's like this. We monkeys have always been a decent people—we haven't made any wars, or oppressed anybody, or built any prisons, or bred poverty and foul diseases and scrawny young, and we don't think **we** ought to have this scandal put over on us.

GOD: Have what put over?

JIM: Why that man is any kin to us.

TANGO: We're decent, we are.

GEORGE: It ain't right. We've never done nothing dirty or mean or crooked, and it ain't right.

TANGO: Our record is clean. We are proud to climb our family tree.

GEORGE: Tango is great on climbing trees.

JIM: We are getting prayers from our own people on earth to have this slander stopped.

TANGO: Man is no kin to us. It's a disgrace.

GOD: Yes, but don't you see, to stop it I've got to give millions and millions of mankind brains, just a little, but some.

JIM: Well, you can do anything.

GOD: Hm.

GEORGE: Won't you help us?

GOD: You are mistaken about anyone claiming man is descended from a monkey. One crowd—the fundamentalists—are as mad as you are that anyone should say man has ascended from the lower animals.

TANGO: Lower? Lower?

GOD: I don't say that. That is what they say; the fundamentalists. The other crowd—the evolutionists—say man and monkeys and all the animals have worked their way up from a simpler form of life much lower. Maybe the very first starting-point was the same, but each has worked out its own destiny by its own will and desires, along its own line, and each is ascended or descended only from itself—man from the long chain ending at present in man, and monkeys from the long chain ending at present in monkeys; but the chain of each is its own.

GEORGE: What's the inside fact?

GOD: What is Tango doing up in that tree? Call him down.

JIM: Tango isn't a him—she is a her.

GOD: Excuse me. Call her down.

JIM: Excuse me. You call her down.

GEORGE: Women have always been equal to men with us.

JIM: And a little more.

GOD: Well, she's got to come down. That's my Tree of Knowledge. If she eats the fruit it will kill her. Fortunately it's a little green. Tango, come down.

TANGO (*From the tree*): What for?

GOD: She's a she all right. You come down from that tree immediately.

TANGO: I don't want to. I want to find some fruit.

GOD: If you don't obey me and come right down I'll take you out of Monkey Heaven and put you in with Billy Sunday.

TANGO: Wait a minute. I'm coming.

GOD: That's a good girl. Peter, have you a cocoanut about you?

ST. PETER: O, gracious Lord, a cocoanut about me! Where would I get a cocoanut?

GOD: I thought you might have the spirit of a cocoanut. Never mind, I'll make one for her.

GEORGE: Now, what are the real facts?

GOD: About the creation of man?

JIM: Yes. Did you make man right off, just like that, and pull a woman out of his side, or how about it?

GOD: Do you see this book I was reading when Peter interrupted me? It is the Book of Life and it is all there. You will find that I debated whether I would make man complete at the start and let him keep falling lower and lower, or to breathe life into a very simple cell and let man and every other creature struggle higher and higher from that single beginning, according to the strength of its desire. It seemed to me the latter plan was more simple, more scientific, more automatic, and that it relieved me of a lot of responsibility. In fact,

I established the universe on general rules, not on special creative acts.

TANGO: That's all right, but can't you stop this slander on our family?

GOD: Only by the working of the general rule. Man must desire intellect and education so much that he will finally achieve them, and quit being a fool.

TANGO: And we suffer meanwhile?

GOD: It seems so. Man will suffer, too, but suffering is the great educator. Man must be educated. Why, look at him. He takes a pride in war. Think of it.

JIM: If we have to wait till he gets brains, it looks pretty hopeless to me.

GOD: It will take a long time. A million years and a million million are but as the falling of a leaf in my sight. Be patient. Now, if you will excuse me, I will return to my reading of the Book of Life. It is intensely interesting. Remember, if man does not exterminate himself by fighting, he will learn wisdom in the countless ages of time to come. Peter, give these cocoanuts to the lady and the gentlemen. Do not be so sensitive, dear people. Man has even likened himself to me, but I don't get mad—I laugh.

(ST. PETER *goes out with the monkeys.*)

## VI

### BIRTH CONTROL

(GOD *has just come in from an inspection of the universe and is warming his hands at a fire.* GABRIEL *is standing by him.* GOD *meditates in silence for a time.*)

GOD: Gabriel, who is Anthony Comstock?

GABRIEL: Lord, don't you know Anthony Comstock, Censor?

GOD: Never heard of him.

GABRIEL: O, Omnipotence and Omniscience!

GOD: Who? Anthony Comstock?

GABRIEL: I was addressing your Godhead. Anthony Comstock is the censor of mortal morals.

GOD: I may be omniscient but I don't understand.

GABRIEL: He is the man you put in charge of the morals of the earth.

GOD: What earth?

GABRIEL: Jesus' earth.

GOD: What are morals?

GABRIEL: Morals, O Omniscience, is to believe that babies are brought by storks, that women are without legs, and before a man can take a woman to wife he must ask the county clerk, and that to drink wine is wicked.

GOD: Oh—ignorance. I never put anybody in charge of anybody's life. (*Shivering*) Gabriel, we haven't had a decent fire since the Devil left. Blow for Peter.

(GABRIEL *blows three blasts and* ST. PETER *enters.*)

ST. PETER: Omniscience, there's no one to watch the gate.

GOD: Good idea. I begin to suspect you are a censor.

ST. PETER: A what?

GOD: A censor. Hand me my slippers.

(GOD *sinks into an easy throne before the fire and* ST. PETER *puts his slippers on him, first kissing his toe.*)

GOD: Peter, did you ever hear of Anthony Comstock?

ST. PETER: O, yes, Omnipotence. He is so pure that you are impure. He is a perfect saint.

GOD: I remember. St. Anthony—that crazy old——

ST. PETER: No, this is another one.

GOD: I was out on the bridge, busy with the Christians and their holy war and the other savages and their wicked wars, and the crops and the weather, and the churches and the jails, and the slums and adulterated milk and infant starvation, and factories and mines, and other earthly things, and the universe generally, when a cloud of special rush prayers commenced to arrive from New York from churches and factory owners, and from my adviser, Theodore, asking me to bless St. Anthony Comstock in his effort to ruin an architect named Sanger.

ST. PETER: What had Sanger done?

GOD: Nothing.

ST. PETER: Nothing?

GOD: Well, yes. He had taken to wife a woman—

ST. PETER: Is that so bad, Omniscience?

GOD: It is risky, Peter—risky.

ST. PETER: Hm. Well. Well.

GOD: This woman, Margaret Sanger, is teaching poor women how to limit their litters of ill-fortuned, misbegotten young.

ST. PETER: O, yes, Lord, my church feels it is wicked to interfere with your sacred laws of life.

GOD: As, for example, in this wonderful great European War. Or in the factories, or the mines, or the slums, or the gallows? Eh, Peter? Let me tell you here in confidence, Peter, your church and all churches have a lot to learn about me. Stir the fire. I wish Satan was back—we had no trouble about fires when he was here. Ha—Hm—Censor. Fool. Censor. Hm. (*Yawns.*) Leave me, Peter. Disconnect the earth.

(PETER *goes out.* GOD *closes his eyes.*)

# VII

## ANTHONY COMSTOCK IN HEAVEN

(GOD *is reclining on a marble bench on one of the piazzas of the universe, listening to the choiring of the spheres.* GABRIEL *is asleep on another bench, his horn by his side.*)

(ST. PETER *comes in.*)

ST. PETER: Excuse me, but——

GOD: Oh, Peter. Cannot I have a little peace, even in Lent?

ST. PETER: But this is very important, Lord. It relates to a lost soul.

GOD: That's not important. Well? Well, what is it?

ST. PETER: There is a soul just outside the gate cutting the most ridiculous capers.

GOD: Why don't you open the gate and let him in?

ST. PETER: He won't come in.

GOD: Send a party out and shoo him in. Peter, the great problem before you today is the falling off in immigration.

ST. PETER: I know it. That's why I came to you about this soul. I have tried to shoo him in but every time anyone starts out, he puts his hands down in front of himself and scampers away like a wild goat.

GOD: Can't you talk to him?

29

ST. PETER: Not till he can find the rag of a cloud to wrap about his middle.

GOD: What does he say then?

ST. PETER: Says he is naked.

GOD: What?

ST. PETER: Says he is naked.

GOD: Well, by myself, did he expect to bring his trunk with him?

ST. PETER: That's all we can get out of him; says he has no clothes on.

GOD: Oh, go back and tell him nobody here wears clothes.

ST. PETER: I have, but he won't listen. Says we are indecent, immoral.

GOD: He's just a plain lunatic.

ST. PETER: I know it, but I dare not draw the line at lunatics.

GOD: That's true. They are your best customers. Are there any of those old halos left?

ST. PETER: Billions of them, but they are pretty rusty.

GOD: Never mind. Take as bright a one as you can find; rub it up a little and set it down by the wall near the gate; a harp, too. Tell him they are his, and everybody get out of sight; then when he steals up, some of you drop down from the wall and boost him through the gate. When you catch him bring him here. A new kind of idiot. From the earth, of course?

ST. PETER: Yes, Lord.

GOD: Of course. Go get him.

(ST. PETER goes out.)

GOD: I am sorry I made the earth—it has been to me like a flea under a monk's shirt. Clothes! Clothes! The poor fool. Gabriel, call Jesus.

GABRIEL: Yes, Lord.

(*Blows a blast on his horn.* JESUS *comes in.*)

GOD: My son, when you were with these pests you call your earthly brethren, did you give out the idea that the naked body is indecent?

JESUS: No Father. How could I be so indecent?

GOD: Of course not. Did you teach that my chiefest miracle, birth, is vile? Male and female—I created them that they might continue the wonder of creation. Did you teach that sex is vile?

JESUS: Father!

GOD: Forgive me, my son. Do you happen to know whether that church of Peter's teaches that nakedness is indecent and that you ascended into heaven with all your clothes on?

JESUS: I know nothing of that church, Father, nor does my good Peter.

GOD: Forgive me, my son. Peter has just been here telling me there is a crazy soul dodging about outside the gate, apparently anxious to get in, but afraid. The poor idiot says he has no clothes on.

JESUS: Poor soul. He mistakes cloth for purity.

GOD: Wait here and we will see. Peter has gone to fetch him. Here they come now. Why, what a curious spectacle.

(ST. PETER *comes in with the soul of* ANTHONY COMSTOCK. *It crouches down, holding its knees close together, and its hands between its thighs.*)

ST. PETER: Here it is, Lord.

GOD: Well, for my sake!

SOUL: Excuse me. Please excuse me. I couldn't help it. He brought me here in spite of my resistance.

GOD: Excuse what? What's the matter with you?

SOUL: For heaven's sake, give me something to put

on. Haven't you a robe or something? O give me a shirt.

GOD: A robe? No! What would I do with a robe? Look at me. I am your God. Your naked God, who created man in his own image.

SOUL: Give me a fig-leaf; just a plain fig-leaf.

GOD: A fig-leaf?

JESUS: Poor lunatic.

SOUL: O, haven't you got just a common little fig-leaf?

GOD: What does he mean?

SOUL: O, don't you know? What Eve put on when she found she was naked.

GOD: When she found she was naked?

JESUS: Father, he is not in his right mind.

GOD: His mind? Call Eve.

(*An angel goes out.*)

ST. PETER: He is crazy. Crazy as the Devil.

GOD: Peter, get it out of your head that the Devil is crazy.

SOUL: No, God, I am not crazy. I am just pure. Can it be that I am the only pure soul in heaven?

GOD: I hope to myself you are.

(EVE *comes in.*)

SOUL: Oh! Oh! Please, give me something to put on.

GOD: Stop squirming. Keep quiet. What's the matter now?

SOUL: A female angel, naked. She is looking at me. Please, please give me something to put on.

GOD: Give him his halo, Peter.

SOUL: O God, I don't want a hat. Haven't you got a fig-leaf? A little one, a second-hand one, any kind of a fig-leaf?

GOD: Stop your cringing and crouching and whining.

Stand up like a decent soul and tell us what you want.

SOUL: I can't stand up. Don't you see I can't stand up. She is looking right at me.

GOD: Everybody is looking at you; you are making a spectacle of yourself. Who is looking at you?

SOUL: That lady angel.

GOD: Well, stand up and look at her. She is Mother Eve. Stand up and look at her.

SOUL: Oh, God!

GOD: O, the Devil.

EVE: Does he not think I am beautiful?

GOD: What is the matter with Eve?

SOUL: She is naked. She hasn't even a fig-leaf?

GOD: But isn't she beautiful?

SOUL: O God—not even a fig-leaf.

EVE: What does he want?

SOUL: I want two fig-leaves—one for me, and one for you. Let us be pure.

GOD: He is too obscene for words. Gabriel, take him away; fumigate him and put him out.

(GABRIEL *leads out the Pure Soul.*)

Now, Peter, I will see no one till after Lent. Has anyone some smelling salts? That soul left a bad smell.

(EVE *presents her salts bottle.*)

GOD: Thank you. A beautiful bottle.

EVE: Crystal. Vulcan carved it for me.

GOD: The good old pagan. I had such an easy time with the pagans—but since these Christians, immortality has hardly been worth living. Let us visit Vulcan.

(*All go out.*)

# VIII

## PROHIBITION

(*Seventh Terrace of the Seventh Plane.* GOD *is looking intently into a crystal bowl which he holds in one hand.* RABELAIS, PAINE, INGERSOLL, MARY WOLLSTONECRAFT *and* MARGARET FULLER *are looking out upon the universe.*)

INGERSOLL: A beautiful sight. How infinite in magnitude, beauty, and design!

RABELAIS: The heavens declare the glory of God, the firmament——

(VOLTAIRE *joins them.*)

VOLTAIRE: Robert, *mon ami.* What is a prohibitionist?

INGERSOLL: One who prohibits.

VOLTAIRE: *Cela va sans dire.* But what does he prohibit?

INGERSOLL: Everything he doesn't like. An egotist, a fanatic. Who should know better than you? Were you not prohibited even to think? A prohibitionist prohibits anything his little egotistic, narrow, tyrannical mind does not approve of—political, religious, social—speech, prayer, amusement, drink. It is "Live *my* way or go to jail." They invented hell as a kind of jail. Your old friend, Torquemada, was a prohibitionist. By the way, where is Torquemada?

VOLTAIRE: Here comes Peter. We'll ask him.

34

and the crozier was only a broom that was standing in the corner. But soon he fell asleep and his cure began from that moment.

VOLTAIRE: Well?

RABELIAS: "Well?" *Ma fois.* Yes, "Well"—it is well. Can you not see from this the value of faith, and the usefulness of theology?

VOLTAIRE: I see that I shall not be led out into a quagmire and my own question be lost. Robert, *mon ami,* what is—are—prohibitionists? They exist only in your country. Are they some sect of fanatics, like whirling dervishes?

INGERSOLL: Well, yes. Fanatics. Prohibitionists believe in intemperance.

VOLTAIRE: Intemperance? *C'est à dire?*

INGERSOLL: Yes. They are intemperate in all things. They hate temperance, tolerance, moderation, self-restraint. They believe in force—moral reform by police clubs and jail. They reject education. They hate freedom of soul.

Voltaire: *Très curieux.* But why?

INGERSOLL: Because they are intemperate. Why are there always people so cocksure of their own wisdom that they will save the world if they have to burn it? Don't ask me why. You ought to put that question to our friend over there with the crystal bowl.

VOLTAIRE: Yes, presently. But what do they prohibit?

INGERSOLL: Everything they do not care for themselves—theatres and baseball, cigarettes and bathing suits, short skirts and long skirts, and just now in my once-beloved country they prohibit whiskey, brandy, beer, wine.

RABELAIS: Prohibit wine! God's gift. The sacra-

ment.   No country would submit to that.   How can
you have a wedding feast without wine?   Remember
Cana.   How can you have a baptism without wine?
How can friends meet and make merry without wine
or part and be sad without wine?   And most of all,
how can you cook without wine, and what of the holy
sacrament?   The very blood of the earth—the blood
of our Blessed Lord and Redeemer?

INGERSOLL:  O, you may meet, but you need not be
merry, and you may part and the sadder the better.
As for good cooking, prohibitionists know nothing
about it.   As for the holy sacrament, it can be given
in water colored with the juice of the non-intoxicating
beet, or with "Whistle."   Many prohibitionists recom-
mend "Whistle."

RABELAIS:  "Whistle?"  *Mon Dieu.*  "Whistle?"  For
what should we whistle?

INGERSOLL:  For the good of your soul.   "Whistle"
is a sort of soda pop—much advocated by some en-
thusiasts for the Lord's supper.

RABELAIS:  But what have such things to do with
the sacramental wine of the last supper?

INGERSOLL:  If water can be changed to wine, why
not "Whistle"?

RABELAIS:  O, *mon Dieu.*

PAINE:  Robert, like yourself, François, is a humorist and humorists are not always to be trusted.   He is
not fair to the prohibitionists.   They are very sincere.

VOLTAIRE:  Pests of the world.   Sincere fanatics.

PAINE:  These sincere——

VOLTAIRE:  Pests——

PAINE:  —prohibitionists see that drunkenness is an
evil.

RABELAIS:  But the whole world is not drunk.

Drunkards are few. And who gets drunk on wine—
our Lord's drink?

VOLTAIRE: Your friend of the wild goose chase, *par
exemple.*

RABELAIS: Not on wine—on cognac—and he one
among millions of sober people. France is not a country of drunkards, nor Italy. Wine-drinking peoples
are not drunkards. But the holy sacrament—does
Jesus know about this?

PAINE: I do not think so. The Christian churches
are the most active in this prohibition business, and
they, as you know, know nothing of Jesus.

RABELAIS: I will ask Jesus. Wine prohibited by
force. I——

PAINE: Presently.

RABELAIS: Burgundy — Bordeaux — Sauterne —
Hock—Liebfraunmilch—Ha! Milk of Venus prohibited and the great doctor. Berncastler—Doctor—
Lachrymae Christi from the hot slopes of Vesuvius—
Ha!—tears of Christ—Christ's tears prohibited—sacrilege! Chianti of Tuscany—old Barolo and violet-
smelling Falernian. By the shades of Quintus Flaccus
—where is he? Where is our beloved Horace? Falernian forbidden by edict of some chop-swollen,
paunch-bloated tyrant.

PAINE: No. No. Prohibitionists are as lean as a
dried eel.

RABELAIS: Christians—Ha! What do they know
of the gentle Christ, and God, the Father, Giver of all,
tolerant to all, maker of all—even of temptation—and
the dear, gentle, loving Christ who denied force? Did
they ever behold the great miracle? Pruners in the
vineyards singing songs of the mystery. Silent plough-
men with patient mules, carefully scoring between the

vines, but not too deep lest they wound the breast of
Dionysus.   Filled with the glory of God, at last he
wakes, Dionysus comes.   Little velvet buds, pink as the
nipples of a young mother, put out their lips and suck
the sun.   Delicate roots in their dark birth-chamber
suck the milk of the mother—the stems urge to viney
length and the leaves spread their loving shade above
the small, green flowers that smell so sweet after rain.
By the beneficent sorcery of God, these, even as you
look, turn to emerald beads and beads of jade.   Under
the hushed moon as well as under the sun, the noise-
less miracle is worked till the purple goblets are full.
Then the pickers clothe the hillsides with song.   Young
men and women tread the great tubs, their sun-browned
legs dyed as with Tyrian, and the pressers swing on the
arms of the wine press.   Presently the purple juice
quickens, moves, shouts aloud: "He comes, Dionysus
comes."   Jesus is risen—in the eternal resurrection of
eternal life.   Wine is born; sacred symbol of the life to
come.   Secretly it is born in the quiet of the caves as
in the quiet mystery of the womb or the grave.   Ha!
Prohibit God's gift?   Prohibit God's miracle?   Who
are these misbegotten, mischristened Christians who
have forgotten the wine, the oil and the bread—wine
that maketh glad the heart of man, wine that is a drink
offering to the Lord?   Do they remember the vineyards of Eschol and of Engedi, or the feast of Cana,
or the patient tolerance of Christ?

PAINE:   But—

RABELAIS:   Let these judges of men go to the Book
of Judges and be judged.   "Shall I leave my wine which
cheereth God and man?"   There.   I stop there—I take
my stand with God—"Shall I leave my wine which
cheereth God and man?"   No—ten thousand times no.

*Eheu!* I forgot I have no throat. *Hélas! Hélas!*

PAINE: But I was going to say, the prohibitionists
see that drunkenness is bad and it makes no difference
if only one man gets drunk and beats his wife or kills
his friend, or starves his children—for that one the
thousands of temperate must be prohibited. They will
talk of the great rejoicing over the lost lamb which was
brought back to the fold and forget the flock of thousands that furnish the wool.

INGERSOLL: Did Jesus intend to drag his black lamb
back into the fold with a ring in its nose, sheep-dogs
biting its throat and the shepherd beating it on the buttocks with an iron crook?

PAINE: Presently, we will ask Jesus—presently.
Now our prohibitionists—it is a long word. Now, our
"Drys" see that drunkenness is produced by alcohol,
so they argue, no alcohol, no drunkenness. Wine, beer,
and spirits contain alcohol, so no wine, beer, or spirits.
The beer of little alcohol as bad as the spirits with
much. There you are.

VOLTAIRE: Simple.

INGERSOLL: As simple as the prohibitionists. It
omits life, the thirst for soul freedom, the right to be
one's self, a natural appetite and a poverty disease all to
be cured by force.

RABELAIS: Believe me, my friends, it has never been
done. Force never pushed the world forward an inch.

PAINE: No, it has never been done. It will fail.
But let us be fair as to motive. We are not responsible
for their intelligence.

VOLTAIRE: God be thanked.

MARGARET FULLER: Was the human soul created
by a policeman's club?

RABELAIS: Will the younger generation not know

paregoric? Ha! There lurks a demon in paregoric, and spirits of ipecac, wine of pepsin. Shall we be prohibited our beloved drugs? Aesculapius! Galen!

PAINE: Having decided that alcohol is the cause of all evil—naturally one drop is as bad as a bucketful—beer as bad as whiskey, wine as bad as brandy or gin. Your prohibitionist is emotional and never reasons.

INGERSOLL: Naturally. One capable of reasoning could not be a prohibitionist.

SWEDENBORG: I have been listening. How opposite to tolerance prohibition is. How opposed to education and persuasion. How opposed to Christ.

VOLTAIRE: Of course. Prohibitionists are Christians, and Christians are always opposed to Christ. You cannot believe in Christ and belong to the order of Christians.

PAINE: Certainly not. Christ insisted on the doing of his word, not the saying of it.

SWEDENBORG: But in my country, where grows no vine, the drinking of spirits in that hard, cold land became an evil habit. We sent a commission of divines, teachers, legislators, and business men to examine this prohibition in your country, Robert, and they found it did not prohibit, but did breed lying, law-breaking, and drunkenness.

PAINE: The "Drys" have now written prohibition into the Constitution of the United States; that Constitution with which I fancy I had something to do—through my friend Jefferson—the Bill of Rights, for example.

RABELAIS: Rights—what rights? They cannot speak, write, or drink. What other rights are there? No use to prohibit thought. They do not think.

SWEDENBORG: In my country beer was made free

of tax or license, wines were taxed by the alcoholic content on a rising scale, and the government itself became the dispenser of strong drink. It changed the country to the most temperate in Europe except Italy. Yet no prohibition anywhere.

PAINE: I have told you that to emotional fanatics the rights of millions are as nothing; all they see is the one pitiful drunkard.

RABELAIS: Aren't the vastly larger herd of fine white goats worth saving? Must they be debased and degraded that some scabby sheep may be helped?

VOLTAIRE: But the price—the open saloon is gone but licensed and illicit distilleries are still making alcohol—now the price?

PAINE: O, the price is heavy. Millions on millions of taxes wasted on cruiser fleets, speed boats, armies of police, scouts, spies, stool pigeons.

VOLTAIRE: Yes. Yes. That is the money, but the morale, the manhood—the real price?

PAINE: Lying, spying, betraying, cheating, bribing, corrupting have been made the national game. The national morals is law breaking, and corrupting of officials a successful fine art. High federal courts swamped with cheap police court work, prohibition judges giving vindictive sentences, judges sympathetic with freedom giving nominal ones. The most flourishing of all the infant industries is "bootlegging."

RABELAIS: *Qu'est-ce que c'est que ça?*

PAINE: Illicit traffic in wines and liquors.

VOLTAIRE: Ah, smuggling?

PAINE: Yes and more. Every family has its own brewery or distillery in the kitchen, or winery in the cellar. Grapes may be lawfully bought and squeezed. If the juice turns to wine, whose fault is it?

RABELAIS: Fault! It is the act of God. Do these pro—what'd you call-'ems?—not forbid grapes also?

INGERSOLL: They would if they could. Your fanatic is like a mad bull. He marks his target, lowers his head, and charges with closed eyes. Your prohibitionist sees nothing. Waste of millions of money, national lawlessness and corruption, boys and girls carrying gin flasks, seductions, abortions, drug habits, poisonous concoctions, and moral degeneracy increasing mean nothing to him—he sees only the one weakling and the drop of alcohol.

PAINE: Ah! But, Robert, the worst cause that they fail to see is that the drunkenness of the rich is a weakness of a few among the few idlers of society, and will take care of itself under the laws of nature. But the larger drunkenness—the drunkenness of the workers, the toilers, the poor, underpaid and underfed masses—is a longing, a disease bred from poverty. Abolish poverty and the people will abolish drunkenness by education and natural inclination, as a sickly plant becomes strong with sunlight and nourishing soil.

INGERSOLL: What would you advise to abolish poverty, Thomas? Socialism, single tax, anarchism, communism?

PAINE: I care not what you begin with, but let the experiment begin. Only by practice can any social theory be tested.

VOLTAIRE: Hélas! Hélas! It is not "price" they pay, but God's fearful *penalty* for attempting to break his eternal law of freedom of soul, freedom of body, of appetite—freedom of growth, growth by education, not by force. Let us now go over to Him. See, He is still watching the crystal bowl he holds in his hands. How intently He looks into it.

(*They all go to where* GOD *is.*)

PAINE:  You speak to him, François Marie.

VOLTAIRE:  Omnipotence, Omniscience.

GOD:  Excuse me, ladies and gentlemen.  I was lost in contemplation of the wonder and beauty of my own creation.  Gather about me—look into this bowl. Mary, what do you see?

MARY WOLLSTONECRAFT:  I see a finely bubbled liquid, new bubbles constantly rising, and I hear a gentle hiss—it seems to be alive.

GOD:  It is alive, Mary.  Life.  Life.  It is fitting that you, a life-bearer, should detect this life.  It is the growing of countless billions of plants—the marvelous yeast plant.  Do you know the miracle of its growth and fruit?

MARY:  No, Lord.

GOD:  The liquid is the extract from grain of the earth—Jesus' earth.  That grain by a marvel all its own, through sunlight and rain has stored up starch in each little seed, and that starch has turned to sugar here in this bowl, and these billions of unseen plants, unseen to your eyes, even as you look, are feeding on the sugar, turning it into alcohol,—alcohol, fruit of the yeast plant.  A most beneficent fruit if rightly used— injurious if used wrongly, as indeed all my creations are. I have nothing all harmful, nothing all harmless.  Man must determine for himself what it shall be.  Is the growth and fruit not a chain of miracles?

PAINE:  Lord, we came to ask you about alcohol. The prohibitionists forbid all alcoholic drink.

GOD:  Prohibitionists?  Who are they?

RABELAIS:  Fanatics, who instead of flagellating themselves, flagellate their brethren.

GOD:  I don't remember creating——

RABELAIS: *Non, non, non. Bon Dieu,* do not hold yourself responsible. Nobody would dream of creating such things—they create themselves as maggots in carrion.

GOD: Where are they?

VOLTAIRE: On earth.

INGERSOLL: Jesus' earth.

GOD: Of course. Of course. Gabriel, call my son. (GABRIEL *blows his horn and* JESUS *comes in.*)

GOD: Jesus, who are these prohibitionists on that earth of yours?

JESUS: I never heard of them. Men or brutes?

RABELAIS: Brutes.

VOLTAIRE: *Non, non.* François is angry—they are men and women.

JESUS: What is the trouble with them?

RABELAIS: Everything. They attend to everybody's lives but their own.

GOD: As nearly as I can surmise they are followers of your friend Mahomet and abstain from all alcoholic drink.

RABELAIS: Abstain. Who cares if they abstain as Mussulmans do—that is their own affair. That is soul freedom. But they forbid other folk, forbid wine, by *force*—mark you, by *force*—your wine of Cana and the wedding feast, the wine of your last supper. Ha! *Mon Dieu,* it is unspeakable. To forbid by force and clubs the color, the bouquet, the cheer, the staff to old limbs, the marriage feasts, the baptisms, the meetings, the partings, the funerals, the great parting, the splendid festivals—music of zither and of lutes, the dancing of youth, and the last tremulous chat of old age over glasses held in withered hands. Forbidden—forbidden by laws, by armed force, by police clubs, by raids and assaults, courts, jails, fines, disgrace, dirty, sordid tyranny, in your name, gentle Jesus! For drinking your wine! Abstain. Ha! They do not teach to abstain; education is thrown to the dogs, and by force they prohibit. Ha! Today, in that country, at a happy marriage feast, if you the Christ turned water into the best wine of the festival, they would arrest you, dear Jesus, as a—as a—what is it?—a man with boots——

INGERSOLL: A bootlegger. Yes, if today Jesus performed that miracle in the United States every brainless Billy Bryan, Billy Sunday, and Billy-bedamned would be yapping for his arrest and he would be thrown into jail with thieves and murderers.

RABELAIS: Ha! You, the gentle Jesus, a bootleg?

GOD: Peace, François. My son, do you know anything about this?

JESUS: No, Father, I know nothing of any salvation of body or soul by clubs, jails, force and violence, but only by persuasion, education, appeals to intelligence and conscience. Never has force educated or done good—never. I say never.

PAINE: But they call themselves Christians.

JESUS: They take my name in vain. They deny my teaching. What of my life—my whole life? What of my death? If these mean anything, they mean tolerance, persuasion by love, refusal to answer force by force. Father, let me say loud as on that day the thunders of Golgotha were loud: He who forsakes persuasion for intolerance and force is not of me, and I forbid my name to him. I did not pray that there be no temptation and that men be walled about as weaklings, but I prayed that, by soul-struggle, we might be delivered out of evil, triumphant. For the soul to be walled from temptation is like the legs to be walled from walking. Let there be temptation and in the resistance to temptation let there be triumph and growth.

GOD: Do I enforce my laws by force and arrests? Do I not leave the transgressor free to combat temptation, and if he fail to find the error of his ways, to bring upon himself his own punishment? Has this creature man risen from his lower conditions through freedom and by his struggles in freedom only to violate my eternal law of freedom with his forcible restraints, compulsory protection of the weak by persecution of the strong? No growth is ever made by force. The soft heads of the uncurling ferns and rainsoaked weeds push themselves irresistibly through hard earth into the upper light. Such is my way.

JESUS: Father, what must men do to be saved?

GOD: Inhale freedom, and breathe it out through the nostrils.

JESUS: Freedom in what, Father?

GOD: In all things. Go on as he began. Did he not begin in absolute freedom—the struggle for existence and survival of the fittest, the weak to die, the strong to live? But now man makes it his especial business to save the unfit to breed like rabbits, while the fit are killed off.

JESUS: How, Father?

GOD: How? Every way. The social conditions bring poverty. The fit are drafted into the great industrial war by their lords and are outworn and slain; degenerated, annihilated. The unfit breed like flies and their moron progeny are saved. Everywhere the unfit are saved and the fit used up as fuel in a furnace. The fit are enslaved that drunkards may be saved, and above all in those larger combats of the masters—war—

the very choicest of the herd are selected for slaughter and the unfit preserved. Slowly but surely the tide is ebbing—the level of fitness is sinking. A herdsman who managed his herd so stupidly would be counted a fool.

MARY WOLLSTONECRAFT: But would not the struggle for existence mean war and more war till the commercially weaker and yet the finer peoples are extinguished?

GOD: Suppose the cells of man's body each fought for itself to become supreme—how long would the body last? So, also, if each individual in the social group understands that the utmost freedom for all is the only freedom for each, and that union and harmony of all accomplish more than the greatest strength of any and that the whole world is a common village, with common united aims, and trade between all must be absolutely and entirely free, then man will survive and continue to evolve under my eternal conditions; otherwise he must perish.

JESUS: The fool must die in his folly.

GOD: Be not discouraged. Man's life is not the only life. How beautiful is this crystal bowl. Perhaps from such as this—under my eternal laws—will evolve a life more harmonious, more beautiful than man's.

(GABRIEL comes in.)

GABRIEL: Two emanations wish to see you. One says he is you.

GOD: Is what?

GABRIEL: Says he is God.

GOD: What is his name?

GABRIEL: Wayne B. Wheeler, Washington, D. C., Earth. Chieftain of the Anti-Saloon League Clan.

God: O, I dread those people—they are so good, so sure they ought to have my job.

Gabriel: Yes, he says so.

God: Who is the other?

Gabriel: Irving Fisher—professor at Yale.

God: Never heard of him—or it. Show them into the Holy of Holies. I can't be too careful. Maybe he is God. Excuse me, my friends. I will meet you later in the Grove of Wisdom. (*Aside.*) That is, if I am alive.

(*All go out.*)

# IX

## BILLY SUNDAY MEETS GOD

(*The outer battlements of Heaven, near the Earthly Gate, the battlements glittering with angels and archangels; the gate surrounded by guards, their wings restlessly flashing.* ST. PETER *and a group of angels removed some distance back on an eminence. The gate opens a slight crack and the* SOUL *of* BILLY SUNDAY *comes in.*)

ST. PETER:   Michael, I thought the gate opened. Did something come in?

MICHAEL:   No, nothing.

ST. PETER:   Didn't the gate open?

MICHAEL:   Infinitesimally. The smallest soul in the universe couldn't have got in.

ST. PETER:   Certainly, something seems coming this way.

MICHAEL:   Is there a heaven for monkeys?

ST. PETER:   Oh, yes; but this isn't their gate.

MICHAEL:   Well, it's a monkey. Got in by mistake. That's what the gate opened for.

RAPHAEL:   I don't think it's a monkey. See it roll over and over.

GABRIEL:   It's like nothing on earth or in heaven.

GEORGE ELIOT:   Or the waters under the earth.

ST. PETER: I can distinctly hear it bellowing.

MICHAEL: It is frothing at the mouth.

GEORGE ELIOT: Perhaps it is an idiot.

ST. PETER: Well, it is now running toward us very fast, tossing arms and legs. We shall soon know.

(BILLY SUNDAY'S SOUL *runs up, breathless. Puts out his hand to* ST. PETER.)

BILLY SUNDAY: Well, old Pal. Here I am at last. Knocked the ball over the fence. Home run. Beat the Devil to the plate. The dirty, stinking, brimstone scab. He got his filthy claws on me, but I swiped him one in the guts that made him kiss that putrid hoof of his and forget his mother. Where's the kid?

ST. PETER: Who?

BILLY SUNDAY: Your boy Jesus.

ST. PETER: I am Peter.

BILLY SUNDAY: Oh! I thought you was God. That's one on me. Where is God? Didn't he know I was coming? Me and him's been chums. Thick as thieves. For years. Pardners. I sent up more souls than anybody since that guy, Peter the Hermit. Bet I just about filled up this old caboose. Prospered at it, too. Talk about muzzling the ox. You can't muzzle me. I ain't no ox. I'm a bull, that's what I am. And I can make any bull of Bashan look like a Jersey heifer. I've been sending a stream of souls up here, like they was played out of a fire nozzle and at a discount, too. Bargain-counter rates. Trot out a gang of my souls, Pete, heifers and all. They'll want to see the fellow that umpired the game for them. Ain't none of my souls in this bunch?

ST. PETER: What is your name?

BILLY SUNDAY: Who? Me?

ST. PETER: Yes.

BILLY SUNDAY: My name?

ST. PETER: Yes.

BILLY SUNDAY: Don't you know me?

ST. PETER: No.

BILLY SUNDAY: Ain't this heaven?

ST. PETER: It was.

BILLY SUNDAY: Oh, Ballyhoo. Take me up to the boss.

ST. PETER: Who?

BILLY SUNDAY: Take me up to the Old Man. He'll know me. This is ridiculous. I'll bet I've stocked this place. I'll bet you couldn't swing an arm, right paw or south paw, without hitting a soul I've sold his ticket to. While you fellers have been sitting around on clouds, drawing bellyache out of harps, I've been putting pep and ginger into the work. Going right down to hell and kicking the rotten cowardly Devil on his stinking tail and dragging souls out of the brimstone by their hair, and them in the baldheaded row by the slack of their breeches. Take me up to God. He'll know me. I ain't got no time to waste on porters and gatekeepers.

GEORGE ELIOT: Crazy!

MICHAEL: I don't understand him.

RAPHAEL: There's a mistake. He doesn't belong here.

ST. PETER: Gabriel, take him to the Throne.

BILLY SUNDAY: Did you fall guys ever get left? Pete is on to his job.

(*Puts his thumb to his nose and wiggles his fingers at the angels. Goes out with* GABRIEL.)

#### SCENE 2

(GOD *is on the throne of the universe.* JESUS *is standing beside him and millions of angels shine on either hand.* GABRIEL *and* BILLY SUNDAY *approach.*)

GOD: What is it, Gabriel?

GABRIEL: Peter sent me with this. We don't know what it is.

BILLY SUNDAY: It's me, God. Your pardner, Billy Sunday. You know my holler. I'll bet I've shook that throne a thousand times and made the Devil run like a yellow cur with a tin can and a bunch of firecrackers to his tail. I fought the old Brimstone Belcher to the finish, but I had to take the count at last, and here I am. Where is your wife and my brother, Jesus?

GOD: Jesus, is this your brother?

JESUS: I do not know him.

BILLY SUNDAY: Why, I have introduced you and your father to some of the biggest audiences you ever had. Glory! Glory! The Devil is turning poor sinners on his fork in the fires of hell. Too late for them, not too late for you. Come to Jesus! Come to Jesus! Glory! Glory! Salvation is free. God has got his foot on the Devil's neck, holding him while you can jump into heaven. Be quick! Jesus holds open the gate. Come to Jesus! Glory! Glory! Don't wait a minute. Come to Jesus now! Now! Right now! . . . That's the stuff. Recognize it?

GOD: No. Terrible. I never heard of you.

BILLY SUNDAY: Why, this place must be jammed with souls I sent here.

GOD: No. Not one.

BILLY SUNDAY: Not one?

GOD: Are there any, my son?

JESUS: Not one.

BILLY SUNDAY: Where are they?

GOD: I don't know. I never heard of you.

BILLY SUNDAY: Are you sure this is heaven and that you are God?

GOD: No. Not sure I am God—but this is heaven.

BILLY SUNDAY: Well, I want to tell you right here if this place isn't packed with my souls like a circus-tent on the fourth of July, it isn't the old, reliable, genuine heaven we were brought up to. Someone's been asleep at the switch.

GOD: This is heaven, and none of your souls are here.

BILLY: They must be somewhere.

GOD: Not necessarily. The cosmos is so very large and fanatics are so infinitely small.

BILLY SUNDAY: Well, something is wrong. I must have got into the wrong pew. Aren't you Jesus of Nazareth in Galilee—that was?

JESUS: Yes.

BILLY SUNDAY: Well, I've been calling you my brother ever since I began to hate Satan, as loud as I could holler.

JESUS: My brothers neither hate nor holler. They are the pure in heart, quiet, without malice, whose law is love.

BILLY SUNDAY: I guess there is some mistake. Is there any other heaven?

GOD: Many of them. There is one for African savages who shout and howl and jump around as you did just now. Maybe you will find your friends there.

BILLY SUNDAY: Why, there is Herman Morgen-stern. I sent him to hell. He kept a family beer garden on Fourth Avenue in New York, that cesspool of sin. I sent him and the whole rotten, putrid, stinking, cowardly bunch of saloon-keepers lower than hell. They are so low down they will need an airship to reach hell. What is he doing here?

JESUS: I liked him. He was a gentle, charitable soul.

BILLY SUNDAY: But kept a beer saloon.

JESUS: I lived with publicans and sinners.

BILLY SUNDAY: And there is Margaret Hartwell. She had an illegitimate child. She sold her body. She was a harlot. I sent her to hell. How did she get here?

JESUS: I liked her. The one with her is Mary Magdalen.

BILLY SUNDAY: She sold her body.

JESUS: Who sold her body?

BILLY SUNDAY: She did, Margaret Hartwell.

JESUS: Are you sure? Did you ever think that your friends, the captains of industry, the money changers, the rulers of society, and the church that steals my name to serve them, sold her body?

BILLY SUNDAY: Oh, you are wrong there. The rich, powerful people are my best friends.

JESUS: It is easier for a camel to go through a needle's eye than for a rich man to enter into heaven.

BILLY SUNDAY: They pay liberally, I teach their slaves to put their trust in God and the hereafter, patiently submitting to the masters now. I was booked two years ahead when I cashed in.

GOD: When you what?

BILLY SUNDAY: Cashed in. Hopped the twig. Croaked. Died.

GOD: Gabriel, what is that bad smell?

GABRIEL: I don't know. I have noticed it ever since this got in.

# X

## THE UNITED STATES MUST BE PURE

*(After a plunge in the River of Life,* GOD *is lying on the bank, sunning himself. A* VOICE *is heard.)*

VOICE: O God—O God—O God.

GOD: Well—well—well.

*(*SUSAN B. ANTHONY *rushes in.)*

SUSAN: O God. They won't let Vera in.

GOD: Nonsense. We are not so small as that. Heaven is open to all.

*(*CARRIE NATION, ANTHONY COMSTOCK, BILLY SUNDAY, WILLIAM JENNINGS BRYAN, ROBERT INGERSOLL, VOLTAIRE, *and* RABELAIS *come in.* CARRIE NATION, ANTHONY COMSTOCK, BILLY SUNDAY *and* BRYAN *are in great excitement.)*

SUSAN: No, not heaven. She doesn't want to get into heaven.

VOLTAIRE: Nobody does.

RABELAIS: Not even the Holy Papa.

VOLTAIRE: And he so privileged.

SUSAN: They won't let Vera into the United States.

GOD: What United States?

INGERSOLL: Earth.

GOD: Ah! Why should she wish to get in there?

VOLTAIRE: Because she can't.

SUSAN: It is outrageous. They let Lord Craven in.

GOD: Lord? What Lord? Who did you say?

SUSAN: Yes, the Earl of Craven; they let him in, but they won't let Vera in.

CARRIE NATION: And a good thing.

GOD: Is she?

CARRIE NATION: No, she isn't. That's why.

ANTHONY COMSTOCK: She is not pure. Not pure as we are. Not pure as the United States is.

BRYAN: Not pure as we are.

BILLY SUNDAY: Not pure as we are.

GOD: Well, that's something in her favor.

BILLY SUNDAY: She is a scarlet woman, and if I had my way, Old Man, she'd be toasting her toes at the hottest fire in hell.

GOD: Yes. I know you are a Christian. Well, what has she done?

CARRIE NATION: She ran away with a married man.

GOD: Did she love him?

CARRIE NATION: She did. She did, and he married.

SUSAN: A woman doesn't dare all except for love.

GOD: Then it's all right.

CARRIE NATION: All right? All right?

GOD: Don't shriek so, Carrie.

ANTHONY COMSTOCK: All right?

BILLY SUNDAY: All right?

GOD: Did you hear what I said? It is all right, if she loved him.

CARRIE NATION: But the man was married to another woman.

GOD: He should leave her if he had ceased to love her. My law is Love—my great eternal law—Love sanctifies all.

BRYAN: Sanctifies adultery?

GOD: Yes. It even sanctifies what—you call marriage. If marriage is with love it is holy; if not, it is adultery.  If adultery is love open and honest, it **is** marriage.  Love sanctifies the making of marriage and the breaking of marriage where there is no love.  Love is my cosmic law.  All human laws must fall before it.

(THE WOMAN TAKEN IN ADULTERY *comes in with* JESUS.)

ANTHONY COMSTOCK:   But, Omniscience, you do not understand; this Vera, Countess of Cathcart, was really an adulteress.

GOD:   Not if she loved openly, purely.  The stain of adultery is the concealment of love; the lying, the deceit.  She did not do that.  If she openly lived my law of love, she was a pure woman.

ANTHONY COMSTOCK:   She broke the law.

GOD:   It is your law that is foul, false, a denial of love.

BRYAN:   But, Lord, where will such doctrine lead to?

GOD:   To heaven.

BILLY SUNDAY:   See here, Pardner, do you mean to tell me——

GOD:   No.  I don't.  It would be a waste of time.  Take him away.  He still smells.

(BILLY SUNDAY *is led out.*)

CARRIE NATION:   O Lord.  But she was taken in adultery.

THE WOMAN TAKEN IN ADULTERY:   And I was forgiven all.

JESUS:   Love understands all.  Love never faileth.

ANTHONY COMSTOCK:   Well, the good, pure people of the United States will never forgive her, will never let her come among them.

GOD:   I forgive and I approve.  She may come here.

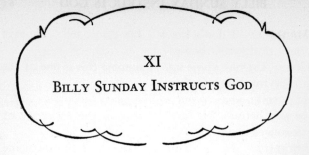

## XI
### BILLY SUNDAY INSTRUCTS GOD

(GOD *is on the Lower Celestial Terrace, meditating.*)

GOD: Gabriel.

GABRIEL: Lord?

GOD: Have those angels practice further away. It is frightful. Where are they from?

GABRIEL: The earth.

GOD: Ah, yes, I remember. The Pill. They always ask for harps. What possesses them with the idea that every soul on earth is a harp-player? Couldn't you get some of them to take up the horn?

GABRIEL: I will try, Lord.

GOD: Do. And have them move further away.

GABRIEL: Yes, Lord.

(*Enter the Archangel* MICHAEL.)

GOD: Well, Michael?

MICHAEL: Billy Sunday wants to see you.

GOD: Who?

MICHAEL: Billy Sunday.

GOD: You mean Holy Sunday, that Christian wreck of a Pagan festal day?

MICHAEL: He's a Christian, all right. Don't you remember that epileptic soul from the earth we fumigated and sent to the Medicine Men's heaven?

GOD: Yes. What does it want?

MICHAEL:   I don't know.   He won't tell.   He says he only deals with bosses.

GOD:   Let him come up.   I suppose this is one of the penalties for being God.

(MICHAEL *nods to one of the guards who goes out.*) Is he any better?   He had fits and all the vulgarity of earth stewed from him.

MICHAEL:   He is about the same, but the medicine men are nearly dead.   He says he has them all backed off the map.

GOD:   What does that mean?

MICHAEL:   I don't know.   None of us knows his language.   Here he comes.

(*Enter the Soul of* BILLY SUNDAY. *He nods familiarly to* MICHAEL *and* GOD.)

BILLY SUNDAY:   Hello, Mike.   Howdy, Pardner.   Say, I've got a jim-dandy scheme.   If you'll come up with the dough, I'll wake up this old morgue and put it on the map.   Make it pay, too.   I can pack heaven so tight the fleas will squeal, and all I want is the gate-receipts for the last performance.

GOD:   Did you want to speak to me?

BILLY SUNDAY:   Sure.   Don't you hear me shouting? I want to bring this old, played-out bunkhouse of yours right up to date.   I've done it for lots of bigger places— Philadelphia, Brooklyn, Boston, Portland (Oregon).   I used to live near there.   I'll make it a regular Coney Island.   The crowds will bust the walls.   Jokes, weeps, vaudeville stunts, shoot the chutes, and mobs you can't get through without tearing your wings off.   I can do it.   I done it on earth and I can do it here.   Say, I've converted all those black and yellow medicine men down below.   I out-howled them, out-drummed them and out-frothed them.   They are regular Christians now: weep, shout, froth at the mouth, and howl for salvation for keeps. Say, you oughter see me lead 'em. Except for color, you couldn't tell 'em from real Christians. Say, you ought to hear those Africans come in on the home-stretch with:

> "I'm a lubber, lubber, lubber of de Lawd,
> "I'm a lubber, lubber, lubber of de Lawd.
> "Jesus is my brudder; Mary is his mudder,
> "Baptized in de blood of de lamb."

All the tom-toms beating, the pebbles in the gourds rattling, the black souls groaning and shrieking. It's real religion. Say, those tom-toms gave me a great idea. They work a crowd up to beat the band. Better than my chorus-yellers. They get the congregation looney in double-quick time; all ready for the Holy Ghost. O, I kin work it. Watch me. I used to use flags, singers, and exhorters, and it cost good money; but, believe me, the old original Tommy-tom for a nickel has got 'em all beat a mile. Say, no weak-minded person can hold out against that steady old thump, thump, thump; and pretty soon the brain reels, and with a yell they come to Jesus. Say, we call them old Nigger Medicine Men savages. Take my palaver for it, in true religion they can give us cards and spades. They are gospel sharps all right, all right, and I ought to know. Say, did you ever hear that nigger camp-meeting song about me?

GOD: No. I don't think that has reached here yet; or maybe I was listening to some other hymn of the universe.

BILLY SUNDAY: It's great. Goes like this:

"Mars Billy Sunday's come to town,
O, my Lord;
A-kickin' up and a-kickin' down,
O, my Lord;
He tear de air and he tear his clo'es,
He lead de devil 'round by de nose;
O Lord, de brimstone smell where he goes
Sunday, Monday, Saturday, Sunday,
O, my Lord!

Billy save de blackest souls in a heap,
O, my Lord;
A dollar apiece, and dat's dirt cheap,
O, my Lord;
He stand on his toe and he stand on his head,
His tongue hang out till he almost dead;
'Whoop', 'Hell fire', 'Glory' is what he said.
Sunday, Monday, Saturday, Sunday,
O, my Lord!

Billy knows de Lord, like he made him, 'most,
O, my Lord;
He say 'Ole pal, how's de Holy Ghost?'
O, my Lord;
And he call to de Lord in a mighty shout,
'God spit on your hands and help me out,
And we'll drag dis sinner out by de snout,'
Sunday, Monday, Saturday, Sunday,
O, my Lord!"

Say, ain't that great stuff?  Well, what do you say?

GOD:  I don't say anything.

BILLY SUNDAY:  Well, where were you?  Didn't you get me?  I propose to convert heaven to Christianity. Have a red-hot, old-fashioned revival meeting.  Run out of town all your publicans and sinners, wine-bibbers and scarlet females.  No noise.  No loud laughter; no singing; no drinking; no joy; all as quiet and clean as the cemetery at Gary.

GOD:  What is Gary?

BILLY SUNDAY:  The Steel Trust town.  They are all friends of mine.  You know the Rockefellers?  John, Jr., was going to syndicate me.

GOD:  What is that?

BILLY SUNDAY:  Get salvation on to a business basis and keep the discontented workmen quiet.  Say, I'll tell you.  I'll convert this whole place, including Peter. Run Mary Magdalen, Bob Ingersoll, and them infidels out, and all for the last night's receipts; that' all I want, but I want to make sure they're big.  I want to have a talk with my friends Morgan, Harriman, Charley Schwab, the two Johns, and get a line on the last night's checks before I start.

GOD:  The persons you name are not here.

BILLY SUNDAY:  Not here?  O, that settles it.  Now I know this is not heaven.  How can I get out of here?

GOD:  Just go.

BILLY SUNDAY:  Where shall I go?

GOD:  I might suggest hell.

BILLY SUNDAY:  I thought you had abolished hell.

GOD:  I have.  But I will give you an old corner and I am sure you can start one of your own.  Take it away, Michael.

MICHAEL:  Where?

GOD:  Anywhere—Anywhere.  Out of the universe, if possible.

# XII

## A Fly Bothers God

(GOD *is seated on the summer veranda of the universe. His head is sunk on his chest, over which flows his ample beard. His eyes are closed. A fly buzzes about his fine but rather prominent nose. He occasionally slaps at the fly, without opening his eyes.*)

(ST. PETER *enters.*)

ST. PETER:   Lord. Omniscience. Omnipotence. God.

GOD:   What?

ST. PETER:   Were you asleep?

GOD:   Peter, how dare you?

ST. PETER:   Well, your eyes were closed.

GOD:   I was thinking. Well?

ST. PETER:   They are sending up *Te Deums* from all the churches in Petrograd.

GOD:   From where?

ST. PETER:   Petrograd.

GOD:   Where is that?

ST. PETER:   It used to be my burg.  It's on the earth.

GOD:   Oh, yes. The earth. Wasn't it buzzing at my nose just now?

ST. PETER:   I don't know.

GOD:   Some pest was. Well, what about it?

ST. PETER:   They are fighting on earth now, for your sake and patriotism and humanity and democracy and to end war.

GOD: Huh! For my sake. He certainly is a smart Devil. Patriotism! Huh! Bait for silly minnows.

ST. PETER: I guess it was this fly that was bothering you. Why don't you kill it?

GOD: What, the earth?

ST. PETER: No, the fly.

GOD: I never personally destroy the life I have created.

ST. PETER: Why, the whole of life is destruction.

GOD: Yes, but that is the law of life. If I were to kill this fly merely for my comfort, I would be a wanton murderer. (*Slaps at the fly.*)

ST. PETER: Yet you would allow a bird to eat it.

GOD: Certainly. That would be according to my universal law. (*Slaps at fly.*)

ST. PETER: Well, look down on the earth. They are slaughtering one another there by the millions.

GOD: That is my universal law also. Fools are slain in their folly by other fools, who will in their turn be slain for their folly. Their very success in killing means their own death.

ST. PETER: But soon there will be nobody left but women, children, cripples, and idiots.

GOD: The idiots will have a chance at the women— then more idiots; so extinction by natural law. What are they fighting about?

ST. PETER: I don't know.

GOD: Send down and ask. (*Slaps at the fly.*)

ST. PETER: I have. Nobody knows.

GOD: Surely——

ST. PETER: Oh, well, each side says it is to save its own lives and to save civilization and freedom.

GOD: Freedom! If each says that, then be sure both are lying. What is civilization?

St. Peter:  I don't know.  Money, I think.

God:  What else did you say they are fighting for?

St. Peter:  Patriotism.

God:  What is that?  (*Slaps at the fly.*)

St. Peter:  I think it is a kind of grease these people rub themselves with before they go to fight.  It makes them crazy and willing to die.

God:  Who makes it?  (*Slaps at the fly.*)

St. Peter:  I think their kings make it.

God:  Those who are fools enough to want to kill ought to be killed.

St. Peter:  Is that the law of life?

God:  It certainly is.  (*Slaps at the fly.*)

St. Peter:  Excuse me, but about these *Te Deums* from Petrograd.

God:  You don't mean this fly?

St. Peter:  No, hymns of praise.  They are giving you praise for the capture of Przemysl.

God:  Of what?

St. Peter:  Przemysl.

God:  Again.

St. Peter:  Przemysl.

God:  Did Adam name it?

St. Peter:  I don't know, Lord.

God:  Say it again.  (*Slaps at the fly.*)

St. Peter:  Przemysl.

God:  Well?  How do they mix me up with—with —what you just said?

St. Peter:  They are praising and thanking you for its capture.

(God *covers his face with his hands and his shoulders shake.*)

St. Peter:  Why are you laughing, Lord?

GOD: Oh, Peter. This praise. It is like taking his halo from a baby seraph. (*Slaps at the fly.*)

ST. PETER: But, Lord, pardon me. Are you really Russian?

GOD: What do you think, Peter? You've known me for some time.

ST. PETER: I don't know what to think. The Germans say you are German, and the French say you are French. The English claim you; the Russians say you are Russian, and the Turks say you are a Turk.

GOD: Peter, I guess we'd better have a fly-catching bird somewhere around here.

ST. PETER: Why not kill the fly yourself, Omnipotence? It would be the same thing in the end. You have destroyed cities by plague and earthquake because you were displeased with a few men and women.

GOD: Tut, tut! Peter. Don't put those nonsensical lies upon me. Get me a bird fly-catcher. One that has to eat to live. Hurry up! (*Slaps at the fly.*)

(PETER *goes out.* MICHAEL *enters.*)

MICHAEL: They are sending up *Te Deums* to you, Lord, from Paris, for the capture of Neuve Chapelle and the successful advance of the Allies.

GOD: This fly is a perfect nuisance. Where is Peter? (*Slaps at the fly.*)

(*Enter* RAPHAEL.)

RAPHAEL: They are sending *Te Deums* to you, Lord, from Berlin for Von Hindenburg's success in capturing a Russian army.

GOD: Why should it take Peter so long to get a common, little, ordinary fly-catcher? A little bit of a bird. Peter is not what he used to be.

RAPHAEL: Why don't you kill the fly yourself, Lord, or start a frost or disease that will kill all flies?

GOD: Raphael, I have just explained to Peter that I must act according to my own laws. I cannot violate my own ordinances. Ah, here comes Peter.

(PETER *enters with a fly-catcher which at once snaps up the fly.*)

There, thank myself, we may proceed now more comfortably. Peter, do you care to say anything over that fly?

ST. PETER: No, it had no soul.

GOD: Oh, you are sure of that; yet sure men have. Funny old Peter. What were you saying, Raphael?

RAPHAEL: Here is Mahomet.

(*Enter* MAHOMET.)

MAHOMET: God, the only and the true God, the faithful are sending up thanks that you are with them. They have sunk one French and two British ships in the Dardanelles.

GOD: What did I tell you, Peter? It's robbery of a babe to take this praise.

ST. PETER: But, really, what are you, Lord? German, French, Russian, English, Turk, Hindu, Polish, Austrian, or American?

GOD: Ask them, Peter. They will tell you. Ask the peoples of the earth to which of them I exclusively belong.

(*Enter* JESUS.)

JESUS: Father, if you are ever going to stop this horrible slaughter at all, why don't you stop it at once? Why do you let it go on? Can't you stop it?

GOD: Patience, son, it will stop. They will kill each other off. I will attend to the Turks, the infidels and heathen, and you attend to your "brothers in Christ"; your "Apostles of Peace on Earth"; your "Love one another" Christians.

JESUS: Father, you know they are not my brothers nor my apostles. You know they take my name in vain.

ST. PETER: Lord, the Pope is praying to you for peace.

GOD: Oh, is he? Why doesn't he order it himself? Aren't you supposed to be his agent and to have some "pull" with me? I am afraid the impression will get abroad that I am deaf. If the Pope would order all Catholics of earth to refuse to fight, to refuse to aid war he could end war, if they were good Catholics.

JESUS: But, Father, how long is this to go on?

GOD: Was I ever known to stop a war? Did you ever know me to rescue the dove from the hawk? I do not intend to stop it at all. Let the Pope stop it. He can,—if they are good Catholics. Leave me. I want to close my eyes and meditate on the folly of this little animal.

JESUS: Alas! Alas! They die of their folly.

(*All go out.*)

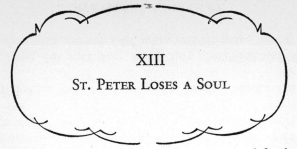

# XIII

## St. Peter Loses a Soul

(GOD *is standing on the upper back verandah of the universe, contemplating his finger nails.* ST. PETER *enters.*)

GOD: Well, Peter, what now?

ST. PETER: I've lost a soul.

GOD: Well?

ST. PETER: I say I've lost a soul.

GOD: It doesn't matter. How did it happen?

ST. PETER: I don't know. I had it with me when I started.

GOD: Where did you put it?

ST. PETER: I didn't put it anywhere. I didn't dare, for fear I would never find it again; I just held it between my thumb and forefinger.

GOD: Was it so small?

ST. PETER: The smallest soul I ever saw.

GOD: Whose soul was it?

ST. PETER: I forget its name. He was a very rich man——

GOD: Did you see if the camel would go through the needle's eye——

ST. PETER: Yes, Lord.

GOD: Did he?

ST. PETER: Yes, Lord. But it took an awful lot of beating. This man had given much to your church.

GOD: My church? Why, Peter, you are becoming

humorous. My church! I have no church, or say as many as there are living souls.

St. Peter:   Well, the church of Jesus.

God:   My good Peter, why will you delude yourself? Neither has Jesus a church. You mean your church —the church of Paul, or of Luther, or the others. But for me and my son, every soul is a church. What was this man's business?

St. Peter:   He sent food to the starving Belgians.

God:   Was that his business?

St. Peter:   No—no—that wasn't his business.

God:   What was?

St. Peter:   He was a munition maker.

God:   What's that?

St. Peter:   He manufactured gunpowder, guns, shells.

God:   Who for?

St. Peter:   Well, for anybody, but just at present for the Allies.

God:   Who are they?

St. Peter:   They are some people on earth who are fighting the Germans.

God:   O yes. That humbug war on the earth. Fools killing fools for their masters.

St. Peter:   Yes.

God:   Why did he manufacture munitions for the Allies?

St. Peter:   Because they paid him, and because the United States, his country, was neutral.

God:   What's that?

St. Peter:   Willing to take money from either side.

God:   So they could kill each other?

St. Peter:   Yes. But he only helped to kill Germans.

God:   What did he have against the Germans?

St. Peter:   Nothing.

God:   They were men and women, weren't they?

St. Peter:   Yes, they were.

God:   Why did this soul manufacture munition things?

St. Peter:   Why?

God:   Yes. For what purpose?

St. Peter:   There is only one purpose: to kill people.

God:   Ah! Thou shalt do no murder. Did he love the plain, common people of the Allies more than the plain, common people of the Germans?

St. Peter:   O, I don't think he bothered about that.

God:   Then why make munitions to kill Germans?

St. Peter:   Well, you see, the Allies paid him well; also they headed off his trade with the Germans.

God:   But so far as he was concerned, anybody's blood money looked good to him?

St. Peter:   He wasn't in the fighting himself.

God:   No, I understand. He was safe. He only took their money.

St. Peter:   Yes.

God:   To give to the churches?

St. Peter:   Well, some of it, and some to starving widows and orphans.

God:   Which he helped make?

St. Peter:   Yes.

God:   I don't like that soul being loose in heaven. In which hand did you have it?

St. Peter:   This one——

God:   Let me see. (*God looks carefully for some time.*) Here it is.

St. Peter:   Where? I don't see it.

God:   No, your sight isn't as good as my all-seeing

eye. Look carefully, there. Under your finger nail, that speck of dirt.

ST. PETER: O, yes, that's it.

GOD: Peter, hold it there carefully and go outside the wall, far into abysmal space. Cast it down to the uttermost depths. Large as I am and small as it is, I will not feel safe till it is cast out of my universe for all eternity.

(PETER *goes out carefully, holding his other hand over the infected finger.*)

# XIV
## Preparedness In Heaven

(GOD *is standing on the Parapet of Celestial Light,
overlooking space. He wears a heavy military overcoat,
tall boots and spurs. A gold helmet hangs by its strap
over his arm and his hand rests on the hilt of his sword.*)

GOD: If Satan should attack now I fear the result.
The walls are in bad shape; we are not prepared. I must
have a campaign of preparedness. Once fully prepared
to resist attack I can myself attack if that seems desirable. Hermes.

(HERMES *enters and salutes gracefully.*)

HERMES: Lord.

GOD: Summon Michael, Mars, Gabriel, Israfel,
Pallas, Aphrodite, and Mary—No, never mind the
women.

HERMES: To hear is to obey.

(*He salutes and goes out.*)

GOD: Immigration has fallen off badly. The most
desirable citizens are all going to hell.

(HERMES, MICHAEL, GABRIEL, ISRAFEL. *and* MARS
*enter.*)

ALL: Lord, we are here.

GOD: Angels, archangels, and gentlemen. I have
sent for you that we may hold a council of war—I
mean of preparedness.

MARS: Ha, of war. (*Rubs his hands.*)

GOD: Nay, I distinctly said of preparedness. By myself, how incredibly stupid that fellow is.

(BOB INGERSOLL, TOM PAINE, JEFFERSON *and* VOLTAIRE *come in.*)

Princes of light, angels, and gentlemen. I intend to make the universe safe for Jesus. To do this we must annihilate Satan, and for this we are not prepared. We must be prepared to resist his attack—or even to anticipate it.

MARS: Good. Prepare for war and you are sure to have it.

GOD: Mars, be quiet. (*Aside*) O, that bellow.

INGERSOLL (*Aside to Voltaire*): Did you ever notice the skulls of these military men? They could slip their collars over their heads without unbuttoning them.

VOLTAIRE: *Les boule-dogs.* No brains, all jaw.

TOM PAINE: Gorillas, and such as these pull the strings on which the poor little marionettes dance to death.

JEFFERSON: Others pull the strings to which these dance.

INGERSOLL: Theirs not to reason why; theirs but to do or die.

VOLTAIRE: Where did you find that military gem, Robert?

INGERSOLL: In the schools. A bread-and-butter bit by a poet laureate of England.

VOLTAIRE: Ha, Poet Laureate. When Pegasus stands at the crib, he sheds his wings.

GOD: Come, gentlemen. We have eternity for war —preparedness, I mean—but no time to waste on poetry.

GOD CALLS FOR PREPAREDNESS

VOLTAIRE:   But, *mon bon Dieu,* that is not poetry.

GOD:   Never mind.   What shall we do to make our heaven, this heaven, the most powerful heaven in the cosmos—prepared to—to—to—defend against any who seem to endanger our supremacy?   Defend.   That's the idea.   All wars are "defensive" wars.

ISRAFEL:   Mobilize and recruit your old Body Guard.

MICHAEL:   Declare the universal draft.

GABRIEL:   I am afraid heaven won't stand for that. Jesus has preached peace too long.

GOD:   With me all things are possible.   We must first frighten them, fill them with fear, then with hate.

GABRIEL:   In what way, Omnipotence?

GOD:   For example, headlines in the *Heavenly Herald*: "Horrible Atrocities of Satan," "Make the Cosmos Safe for Jesus," "Satan Threatens Your Halos," "Satan Disembowels a Cherub," "Satan Rapes the Ten Foolish Virgins," and so on.   Hang the celestial battlements with lurid banners and plaster the Golden Way with fearful posters, showing Satan and his fiends broiling angels on pitchforks, cutting off the wings of cherubs, the Ark sinking with all on board; Noah supporting a fainting daughter in each arm, and the legend "Noah Demands Freedom of the Seas."   Have at every gate and on the steps of the throne posters such as Satan and his fiends clutching virgin seraphs with diabolic intent.

GABRIEL:   But none of this will be true.

GOD:   True?   Of course, it won't.   Don't be a fool, Gabriel.   You can't work up a war—preparedness, I mean—on the truth.   This is war—I mean preparedness —and we simply must lie—the more horrible the lies the better.   Get George Creel and General Crowder to assist you in the publicity campaign to psychologize heaven into hate and fear with lies—they have had experience.

GABRIEL: But about the compulsory draft?

GOD: Do as I tell you. Get them fear-struck and hate-crazy and they will volunteer. Then, too, you can call the forcible draft "Volunteering *En Masse.*" Wilson did.

VOLTAIRE: *O par la messe.* A happy thought. Push them forward with bayonets in their buttocks and whisper in their ears: "Patriots, you are volunteering *en masse.*" "*Vive le Bon Dieu,*" "*Vive Jésus,*" "On, on to Glory, brave volunteers—*en masse,*" "Jesus is a red-blooded fighting man," "Take up the sword of Jesus." "Volunteer—Volunteer," "*En avant.*"

GOD: Now you understand. Psychologize them into hate. Then you can do anything. Only lies will do it. Lie fearfully; lie abundantly. Be not afraid that they will have sense to see through it.

GABRIEL: But how about the teachings of Jesus?

GOD: Pish, nobody pays any attention to him. Tell the people Jesus is all for blood—a sword in each hand. Blow your horn constantly. Make proclamation everywhere that this is a war to end preparedness. I mean a preparedness to end war.

GABRIEL: Omnipotence, I will do my best.

(*He goes out.*)

GOD: Mars, take charge of munitions. I want thirty billions of my new suffocating bolts, two or three thousand of my bombs, any one of which will blot out a universe. This is going to be a preparedness, not only to end war but to end everybody but us.

MARS: It shall be done.

(*He goes out, rubbing his hands gleefully.*)

VOLTAIRE: I hope, Omnipotence, you are sure of "us"?

GOD: Perfectly sure. Israfel, mobilize the Old Body Guard. Put David in command of the slings, furnish them with star pebbles which spread the glory of heaven, this heaven, our heaven, and produce permanent blindness—apply to Gabriel for them. Establish training camps, make every step to war—I mean preparedness—as romantic as possible.

ISRAFEL: It shall be done, Omnipotence, and more.

GOD: Enthuse the girl-angels. Bring the young people together. Together! Understand?

ISRAFEL: I understand.

(*He goes out.*)

GOD: Michael, take charge of the conscription—I mean the volunteering *en masse*. If there is any criticism, or complaint, or resistance, jail them, torture them, obliterate them. We want no objectors, no slackers. This must be a purely voluntary enlistment.

MICHAEL: I will make it voluntary, if I have to choke every angel of them.

(*All go out except* GOD. JESUS *comes in.*)

JESUS: Father, I want to spend my Easter vacation in—Why, Father, you have on all your old Jehovah things and the great presentation sword "To Jehovah from his grateful people."

GOD: Yes. And I have ordered a complete outfit for you—uniform, helmet, boots, spurs, some of my all-destroying bolts, and a sword of flame.

JESUS: For me?

GOD: Yes, for you.

JESUS: Such things for me?

GOD: Certainly—for you.

JESUS: But, Father—why?

GOD: To kill your enemies. We are preparing for war, and when prepared we are going to have one if I have to make it myself.

JESUS: To kill my enemies?

GOD: Sure. Kill your enemies.

JESUS: But I have no enemies.

GOD: Then you ought to have.

JESUS: But I said "Love your enemies."

GOD: Yes, that's what you said, but no one believes it. Your own ministers down on that pill say you never meant it. They are bragging that you are a red-blooded person who can hate just as well as any pirate. They say that you are a regular swashbuckler, dippy for blood.

JESUS: O, Father, let this cup pass from me.

GOD: Don't blame me. Look to your earthly disciples. They are thirsty for war, frothing with hate. Have you heard your man Manning of New York? He wants military training in the schools. But why name names? The whole pack say you are a fighter, a hater, a bloodsucker, that you never meant a word of "Love your enemies," "Blessed are the peacemakers," "Forgive," "Love your neighbor," "Do good to those who have despitefully used you," or "Do unto others as ye would that they should do unto you." It is one cry from all over Christendom—that all this is bunk and that you are a fighter, a bully, a liar—and hate is your gospel.

JESUS: Judas, Judas—poor blind soul.

GOD: My son, I am all for war. The old Jehovah fighting spirit is aroused. But, my son, I will tell you that the cosmos has evolved no more contemptible louse than these same snotty-nosed, snivel-snouted, bag-faced, loose-lipped, double-chinned, lean-bellied, fat-bellied, fat-breeched, prayer-whining, hymn-howling, praise-chanting, self-seeking, place-hunting, pulpit-pounding, wealth-grovelling, war-shouting, hate-spitting, black-souled, white-livered hypocritical cowards of yours who use your name to gild their rotten hearts.

RABELAIS:   *Bravo, bravo, le bon Dieu! Encore. Bis.*

GOD:   The wolves in your clothing hound and persecute your few true followers—the Quakers, Pacifists, Christians. I say *Christ*-ians, not Christians.

PAINE:   And the *Christ*-ians are jailed by Christians for following Christ.

VOLTAIRE:   A joke—a comedy.

JESUS:   My God, my God, why hast thou forsaken me?

GOD:   I have not forsaken you, my son. Your false prophets forsake you. Wolves in sheep-clothing—the monkey-brained, smug-mouthed, oily-skinned, unctuous-souled, sanctimonious-eyed, self-love-bloated, teat-sucking, patriot-shouting Judases. No, I recant that last. Poor Judas does not deserve it.

RABELAIS:   *Bis. Bis.*

VOLTAIRE:   *Il est facile.*

GOD:   Why, down on that spitball of yours a government that calls itself after your name, the Christian Government of the United States—that is to say, some tiger-necked, bull-faced, beetle-browed, bulldog-jawed, tiger-hearted, hog-brained men and this man Wilson have declared your Sermon on the Mount treasonable, and even for circulating it men and women are jailed by these thick-jowled, thick-skulled blood-feeders—these lying General fish Chowders, fish Creels, blood-thirsty judges — Kickshaw — Rickshaw — Kenesaw Mountainous Landis—who sentenced a lot of boys to twenty years of penitentiary hell because they had

I.W.W. cards; and Judge—O by myself—Judge Julius M. Mayer, District of New York, who sentenced Molly Steiner, a mere girl, and four of her boy comrades to twenty years out of their young lives for circulating in New York City a leaflet asking why the United States had troops in Russia, an "ally" country with which the United States was not at war, and two of the boys are already dead with consumption. Pah—"Justice." "Justice." By myself, where is my Recording Angel?

RECORDING ANGEL: Here I am, Lord.

GOD: Write high in the Book of Infamy with apologies to Judas, Jeffreys, and Torquemada — Kenesaw Mountain Landis and Julius M. Mayer, false judges, who vindictively betrayed holy justice they were sworn to serve. Write high above Ananias, father betraying Jacob, and Benedict Arnold the names of Crowder and Creel.

INGERSOLL: Was there not a Julian Meyer?

GOD: Yes. He was human but this Julius was a vampire. Let the names of Julius and Kennesaw be anathema and their descendants shamed forever.

PAINE: Omniscience, may I nominate for a place in the Book of Infamy the officers of the court martial at Schofield Barracks, Honolulu, who sentenced to forty years' imprisonment two young soldiers—Couch and Trumbull—for organizing a communist league?

GOD: No, Thomas, no. The great Book of Infamy is not open to such trash. They are just ₁lain idiots. They carry their brains in a helmet, as butchers carry calves' brains in a bucket.

INGERSOLL: And can slip their collars over their heads without unbuttoning them.

PAINE: Such sentences at least open the eyes of the young recruit to what he may expect.

INGERSOLL: Yes. But think of such brutal cave-dwellers having the life and liberty of young men in their charge.

GOD: Let us close the book for a season.

INGERSOLL: For a season. O, Judas, Judas, in what a bright light I see you now, hanging from that carob tree, a halo on your dropped, repentant head.

PAINE: By comparison with these he seems noble, for he knew not that he had betrayed the world's salvation.

INGERSOLL: He did not betray and then snivel of doing God's work, of patriotism, of the flag of freedom, and saving the democracy and peace of the world. Bah!

JESUS: My Sermon on the Mount is true and they will find it so or perish.

GOD: They say it is against their war.

JESUS: It is—and against all war. It is against this war of yours, Father.

GOD: You mean my preparedness.

JESUS: O, Father. Do not put me to shame.

GOD: But suppose Satan should attack?

JESUS: Father, you know there will be no attack, and you know if he does you are supreme in truth, justice, and love. You know there is no goodness in war. Preparedness invites attack for fear you will attack first. It all invites fear.

GOD: He is our enemy.

JESUS: Love your enemy.

GOD: He has conspired against us.

JESUS: Do good to those who despitefully use you.

GOD: He is back of this very earth war that despises you.

JESUS: Resist not evil with evil.

GOD:   Well—well.

JESUS:   Blessed are the peacemakers.

GOD:   But, my son, for two thousand years I have watched your failure on that pill.

JESUS:   What is two thousand years, Father, in eternity.  If you will let the sun live, they may yet, in the million years or so that you have promised, see that they who live by the sword shall perish by the sword, and the hope of life for any is a full life for all in the world-wide brotherhood of world-wide perfect peace.

GOD:   In a million years——

JESUS:   Yes.

GOD:   Leave us together.

(*All but* GOD *and* JESUS *go out.*)

Come, come, my son.  Live up to the reputation your agents are giving you—your Manning and Landis reputation.  Don't be a slacker.  Let us make the universe safe for brotherly love and me, and for you, my boy. It will all be yours when I am gone.  You can help a lot.  You have a reputation in this love and brotherhood business, and if you would give the angels twenty-minute talks on love and brotherhood and the atrocities of Satan, and the holy cause of making the universe safe for—well—for—you know—for you and me——

JESUS:   But, Father, I meant every word I said on earth, and when I spoke of turning the other cheek and giving the cloak also, it was to make more clear the eternal truth that love, not hate, is the salvation of the world.  I got all this from you, Father.  Am I not your son?  I meant literally to return good for evil—not evil for evil—nor just good for good.  Do not even the Pharisees the same?  Father, you yourself, said "Thou shalt not kill" and I have conscientious objections to murder under any name.

GOD: A conscientious objector. Look down on earth and see where they are—all in jails, in penitentiaries—despised, persecuted, tortured.

JESUS: The glory is theirs—world without end.

GOD: The glory is theirs?

JESUS: Yes, in the ages when newer stars will light the universe with a greater light. Father, I am your son and what I am is of you. Betray me not.

GOD: Though men betray you I will not betray you. Come to my arms, my son.

JESUS: Father, blessed are the peacemakers.

GOD: Gabriel, Gabriel.

(GABRIEL comes in.)

GABRIEL: I am here, Lord.

GOD: Gabriel, blow your trumpet. Call them all here.

(GABRIEL blows his trumpet. MARS, MICHAEL, ISRAFEL and others come in.)

Archangels, angels, gentlemen! Discontinue all military preparations. If Satan comes we will meet him as a brother in friendly discussion.

MARS (To GABRIEL): As a what? In a what?

GABRIEL: As a brother in discussion.

MARS: What's that?

VOLTAIRE (Aside): Look at his jaw.

INGERSOLL (Aside): He could slip his collar over his head without unbuttoning it.

PAINE: His skull—a gorilla. He represents the extreme stupidity of man—war.

ISRAFEL: But, Omnipotence, the walls are broken.

GOD: Put not your trust in walls. All military

preparations will be discontinued.    I have said it.

ISRAFEL:  
MICHAEL: } To hear is to obey.  
GABRIEL:

MARS:    I do not understand.

GOD:    Of course you don't.  Gabriel, proclaim this new truth.  Not to prepare for war is the supreme intelligence of man's reason, the ripeness of his soul.  Beloved Son, let us go view the new-made stars.

(*They go out.*)

## XV
### PRAYER

(GOD *and* JESUS *are standing on the extreme edge of space, looking beyond.*)

GOD: What was that hit me in the ear?

JESUS: A prayer.

GOD: Who threw it?

JESUS: It came from the earth.

GOD: The earth? Oh, yes, I remember. Your earth. Who threw it?

JESUS: Some people of the United States of America who, alas, call themselves Christians.

GOD: Who are they?

JESUS: I do not know, Father. They are strangers to me.

GOD: What does it say?

JESUS: "Almighty God, all wise and all merciful. We thank thee that thou hast kept far from us the slaughter, misery, and devastation of war, and hast permitted us to pursue our peaceful and Christian avocations. We thank thee that our homes are not made desolate, nor the air heavy with weeping. We thank thee that, secure in thy holy protection, we receive the bountiful blessings at thy hands of an unexampled prosperity, and that thou hast turned our factories into hives of industry. Continue thy blessings in the name of——"

GOD: Stop, stop. I know those hives of industry. They are maintaining a bloody war, and for profit. That fellow is smart but he can't fool me.

JESUS: What fellow, Father?

GOD: Satan. That's his prayer.

JESUS: Do you think so?

GOD: Could such hypocrisy, such selfishness come from any of your people?

JESUS: Oh, Father! My people!

GOD: Forgive me, my dear son. But you and I know what that "prosperity" is. Guns, gunpowder, and shells to scatter limbs, heads, and bowels to the air, making widows, orphans, cripples, suffering. War supplies to feed the fire. Murdering at a safe distance for profit. "Love your enemies," "Blessed are the peacemakers," "Return good for evil," "Brotherhood," "Do unto others," etc. Empty—O, worse than empty words. What do you think of it, my son, after two thousand years?

JESUS: Father, Father, why am I such a failure?

GOD: Shall I tell you why?

JESUS: I beseech you.

GOD: Have I ever stayed the rush of the avalanche, the flooding of the tides, or the planets in their courses to save lives or to please you, or myself, or anyone?

JESUS: No, Father; your laws are immutable.

GOD: And my law of life is self-interest. Give power to a few and a short-sighted self-interest will twist that power into tyranny, robbery, and war. The powerful few will hold all others slaves and fight among themselves in competition. "Blessed are the peacemakers," "Love your enemies" are sterile cries, my son, till the people learn—all of them—that love is the best self-interest. Peace, as the greatest earthly blessing, must appeal to a wise self-interest before wars will cease. But it never will appeal while the sordid self-interest of a few lords finds profit in war. These lords must learn or be taught that their own greater self-interest lies in the welfare of all and universal peace; that the earth and its riches belong to all, not to a few.

JESUS: But the poor young men who are dying believe that they die in a noble cause.

GOD: Yes. Toilers in peace, soldiers in war; fools always. Such stupid self-sacrifice is folly, and folly is death.

JESUS: But, Father, they endure so patiently.

GOD: Patience to be slaves is stupidity.

JESUS: Poor fellows, they never had a chance.

GOD: And never will till they awake to their true self-interest. Let them die. Stupidity should always die. If the common people had the sense to join on all sides the world over in common cause against the artificial system which breeds masters, that would be real brotherhood, and I might think them worth saving; but then I would be in them and of them and they would save themselves. As it is, their battles interest me no more than the combats in old cheese. Let my laws take their course. Wars there will be while for each nation the shortsighted self-interest and greed of a few competes for ownership of the earth, and there will be this competition till "civilization" sees its salvation in a free exchange of blessings.

JESUS: Be they never so stupid, the poor are my brethren.

GOD: They need you, yet prefer to follow their masters. What did you do with that prayer?

JESUS: Here it is. Someone is coming.

GOD: Well, speak of the Devil and here he is.

JESUS: I wonder where he is from?

GOD: Your earth, of course.

JESUS: Yes, of course. I wonder what he wants?

GOD: Following up his prayer, I guess.

SATAN: How do you do? I hope you are both well. I am very glad to see you.

GOD: The pleasure is reciprocal. You are always interesting. How are you?

SATAN: Never better. I feel fine. These fruitful days.

GOD: Fruitful?

SATAN: Yes—the war. But I want to see you about——

JESUS: Here it is.

GOD: This hit me in the ear a little while ago. Did you throw it?

SATAN: I don't remember. I do, of course, try to get your ear sometimes. Let me see it.

GOD: Give it to him.

SATAN: Well, I should say not. Whatever you may say of me, you can't say I'm such a rotten, sanctimonious hypocrite as this.

GOD: It is in your style when you play at religion and turn Christian.

SATAN: Oh, you do me a great injustice. This is from Christians who are profiting by the war. They copy my style. However, I admit I am with them. That's what I came to see you about.

GOD: Wait. Here comes Peter in a hurry.

ST. PETER: Oh, Lord. Ha! Hm! Excuse me. Wait a minute till I get my breath. There now. I was afraid this Devil, this enemy of mankind, this unscrupulous——

SATAN: Titles are out of fashion now, Peter.

GOD: Yes, Peter.

ST. PETER:  Would deceive you.

GOD:  Deceive whom?  Me?

ST. PETER:  Not exactly deceive you, Omniscience, but I thought you ought to know that a short time ago he came to the heavenly gate——

GOD:  Who is at the gate now?

ST. PETER:  It is locked.

GOD:  Sorry.  Can't you give up that toll-gate?

ST. PETER:  But, Lord, this war is sending up such a mixed lot.  He said he had a business deal to propose.

SATAN:  Exactly.

ST. PETER:  He said he was in with all the presidents, kings, emperors, cabinets, and overlords on all the sides. And if you would permit him and his friends to keep this war going just one more year, he would make your son independently rich.

SATAN:  Exactly.  It is the chance of a lifetime.

ST. PETER:  I told him to go to hell.

GOD:  Well, Peter, you are always orthodox.

SATAN:  But listen.  You'll admit the few real, true Christians are frightfully poor.

JESUS:  They are.  The *"Christ*-ians."

SATAN:  Well, I'm a partner in all these munition plants and shipyards and so on.  Christ's preachers are all with me, or nearly all.  Those who are not are in jail.  There is a Rev. Mr. Manning in New York who is just wild for blood and militarism.  He knows who butters his bread.  He hopes to be a bishop, and I will make him one.  If you'll let me keep the slaughter going for only one more year we'll have all the money in the world, and I'll give Jesus here a hundred hospitals for cripples, a hundred insane asylums, five hundred orphan homes, and a hundred churches, with the loudest organs and preachers.  I'll put them wherever he likes.    Why, our plant at Bethlehem is making——

JESUS:    Where?

SATAN:    Bethlehem.

JESUS:    Making what?

SATAN:    Money—and guns, shell and shot.

JESUS:    Are you making murder-tools at a place called Bethlehem?

SATAN:    Sure.    Why, our profits at Bethlehem alone——

JESUS:    Father, why hast thou forsaken me?

GOD:    Excuse me, Satan.    Jesus is not feeling well. Please leave us.    Show him down, Peter.

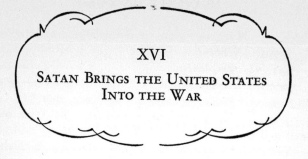

# XVI

## Satan Brings the United States Into the War

(God *is in his mossery, studying lichens and mosses.*)
(Gabriel *enters.*)

Gabriel:   The Devil wants to see you.

God:   Let him come up.

(Gabriel *goes out.*)

I must admit the Devil relieves the monotony.

(Gabriel *and* Satan *come in.*)

(*To* Satan):   Well?

Satan:   I saw a new moss in the Arctic.   A lovely, silver green——

God:   What were you doing there?

Satan:   Went up to cool off.

God:   What had you been doing?

Satan:   Attending a patriotic meeting in the United States of America.   It was great.   So homelike for me.

God:   O, I thought maybe you had found a new hell.

Satan:   I had.   And that's what I want to see you about.   I don't miss hell at all as long as I can keep this war going.

God:   What war?

Satan:   The earth war.

God:   Christ's earth?

SATAN: Yes. Christ's war—that is to say, the Christians' war.

GOD: Well?

SATAN: I want to strike a bargain with you. With the help of my own agents, the press and Christ's preachers, I have just brought the United States into the war, and if you will give me three more years——

GOD: Some time ago you only wanted one year.

SATAN: Wilson hadn't come in then.

GOD: Who is Wilson?

SATAN: O, he is a Presbyterian, a phraseologist, an idealist.

GOD: What's that?

SATAN: One who talks high and acts low.

GOD: I thought Jesus was strong in the United States?

SATAN: Yes. They talk for him and act for me.

GOD: Why did the United States go into the war?

SATAN: National honor.

GOD: Why did the United States go into the war?

SATAN: Patriotism.

GOD: Why did the United States go into the war?

SATAN: To make the world safe for democracy.

GOD: Satan, I have asked you three times why the United States went into this war. You tell me the truth now, or I'll——

SATAN: No, no. I'll tell you the truth. Honest to God. They went in just the same as the others: because the masters wanted it. And Wilson, the egoist, wanted to sit on the world corpse after the war. That's the real truth, but only a few know it.

GOD: That's more plausible.

SATAN: Of course, you couldn't get the people excited if you told them the truth, but you ought to see them fall for "National Honor," "Patriotism," "Democracy," "Germany, the Beast." And the Flag—talk of idols!! In the name of the flag they shout "Freedom," and beat, lynch, jail, and suppress. "Freedom." Of all idolatry, "Flagolatry" is my pet. O, it's great.

GOD: It amuses you?

SATAN: The funniest thing in the world. You ought to see the patriots club their fellow-citizens in the name of freedom and the good old flag of liberty. I nearly die laughing. Haven't you yourself just made a new law: "The stupid shall not inherit the Kingdom of Heaven"?

GOD: Yes. None of these morons going like stupid sheep to the shambles will ever reach here. Well, what do you want?

SATAN: Three years more of it. Now that the United States has come in, I can finish my job and the world in about three years.

GOD: Can you finish the Christian peoples?

SATAN: Sure.

GOD: Well, that's something. Tell Jesus to come here. (*To* GABRIEL, *who goes out.*) What do you propose giving in return for this war concession?

SATAN: Well, most anything. I and my friends on both sides will own the earth by that time and what people are left will be our slaves forever. So you can have anything you want.

(JESUS *enters.*)

GOD: Satan, for certain concessions from me, keeping the earth war going for three years more, agrees to finish the Christians. It is a great temptation.

SATAN: Jesus, I've got a great opportunity for you. The United States is in the war. Taxes by the billions.

Billions, you understand. Money thrown away—lost to the people forever, but not to me and my friends. We will get it. If you will let me have three more years of war, I'll build you churches, temples, tabernacles of unsurpassed magnificence all over the victorious part of the globe. Real stone churches. I will call off the "Hippodrome" "Billy Sunday" style of apostles, and wipe Christians off the earth.

JESUS: Get thee behind me, Satan.

SATAN: Your people are all keen for this war.

JESUS: My people?

SATAN: Yes. Well, the Christians. The ministers. preachers—all but a few scabs and the Quakers.

JESUS: Am I to be always on the cross?

GOD: Go back to your hell upon earth. While the people are stupid, they are yours.

(SATAN *goes out.*)

# XVII

## A Pacifist Enters Heaven—
## in Bits

(GOD *is chatting with a group in the Celestial Rotunda.* ST. PETER *rushes in.*)

ST. PETER: Lord, in all the time I have been gate-keeper I have never had such an experience. I have just let in a soul by sections. It is all in pieces.

GOD: I will see it.

(ST. PETER *goes out.*)

BOB INGERSOLL: In God's name. Here it comes.

VOLTAIRE: *Mon Dieu.* What is it?

RABELAIS: I think it is a sausage.

VOLTAIRE: Oh! His everlasting sausages.

(BATTERED SOUL *comes in, supported by two angels.*)

GOD: In my name, what happened to you? Did you run into a comet on your way up?

BATTERED SOUL: No, Lord. I'm a pacifist.

GOD: A what?

BATTERED SOUL: A pacifist. I believe in Jesus and peace.

GOD: So you are a Christian?

BATTERED SOUL: O, no. I really do believe in peace.

GOD: Did your belief in peace make mince-meat of you?

BATTERED SOUL: Yes. You see, I was at a restau-

99

rant, eating my dinner, and didn't rise when the band played "The Land of the Free."

GOD:  You didn't rise when the band played?

BATTERED SOUL:  Yes—"The Land of the Free."

BOB INGERSOLL:  The Star Sprinkled Buncombe. Has that impossible tune become holy?

BATTERED SOUL:  I guess so.  You have to rise now (unless you're dead) when they play the "Star Spangled Banner" and you have to salute the flag unless you are paralyzed or they beat you up and send you to jail.

INGERSOLL:  O, yes, the "Star Spangled Banner." The flag of the free—the flag born in revolution, the flag of revolution, free opinion.

RABELAIS:  Ah, I see.  This flag is the symbol of freedom, so they beat you up to show you how free you are?

GOD:  Who beat you up?

BATTERED SOUL:  The patriots—the one hundred percenters; those who encourage other people to die for freedom, democracy, etc., while they stay home to beat up.

MARK TWAIN:  Damned cowards, I would say.

VOLTAIRE:  Where did you come from?

BATTERED SOUL:  The land of liberty.

VOLTAIRE:  *Excusez?*

BATTERED SOUL:  The Democratic Republic of the United States.

BOB INGERSOLL:  I wish the two Toms, Jefferson and Paine, and Wendell Phillips were here.

JEFFERSON: ⎫
PAINE:         ⎬  Here we are.
PHILLIPS:  ⎭

INGERSOLL:  Gentlemen, here is what your democracy has come to.  Here is your free republic.  What

A BATTERED SOUL

do you think of freedom and patriotism created by club and jail?    Where is your free speech—free thought?

JEFFERSON:    It is the beginning of the end.

INGERSOLL:    The flag of freedom has become an idol for tyranny.

JEFFERSON:    The symbol remains but the spirit is dead.    The flag is a lie.

INGERSOLL:    The spirit of the people makes the flag —without perfect freedom it is a cheating rag.

PAINE:    If the right of a single one to freely express his opinion at all times, everywhere, be denied, it is tyranny, no matter by what empty name the form of government is called.

WENDELL PHILLIPS:    Absolutely.    If one—anyone —cannot at all times speak freely on any subject whatever, there is no freedom.

PAINE:    The flag has become the symbol of government, and when you are taught to worship the flag, you are taught to worship the existing government though it be a tyranny.    Dangerous, dangerous.    Shall a flag be holier than a man?    A mere symbol become greater than what it stands for?

INGERSOLL (*to* FRANCIS KEY):    You little thought, Key, when you wrote your song to that impossible tune that it would be sending free men to jail.

FRANCIS KEY:    The tune is not mine.    It's an old English drinking song: "To Anacreon in Heaven."

INGERSOLL:    And the mob is drunk on it.    Let me see, when did you write the words?

KEY:    When the English were bombarding Fort McHenry.

INGERSOLL:    Our present "Allies," the English?

KEY:    Yes, they had me prisoner and beat me till I saluted their bloody flag.

INGERSOLL: Sure. Another flag of freedom. Did you love the flag better after the beating?

VOLTAIRE: It was so with us. They put us into the Bastille and we became so loyal that we cut off Louis's head.

RABELAIS: But so foolish not to rise, rather than be beaten. I kissed the Pope's—ahem—toe; and the peasants used to salute my mule.

GOD: Do I understand you were broken to bits because you didn't salute me, or was it the piece of cloth?

BATTERED SOUL: Lots of them have been beaten because they didn't salute the piece of cloth, but I was dissected because I didn't rise when they played the S. S. B.

INGERSOLL: The S. O. B.?

BATTERED SOUL: No. The S. S. B.

GOD: What is that?

BATTERED SOUL: The Star Spangled Banner.

VOLTAIRE: *Morbleu*. In that country one should have an ear for music.

GOD: Is the tune so holy?

BATTERED SOUL: I guess it is. It didn't use to be. Nobody can sing it, but it is our national anthahem.

GOD: Who made it a national—what do you call it?

BATTERED SOUL: Anthahem. Say "anth" and then "ahem." Nobody. It was just played at circuses and shows and Fourth of July picnics till the newspapers called it the N. A. Every country has to have an N. A. now if it has to steal one. "America" is "God Save the King." "Star Spangled Banner" is an old English drinking song. We captured all our tunes except "Dixie."

GOD: What is "Dixie"?

INGERSOLL: That's the national anthahem of the

Southern aristocracy.   They took care of their slaves but didn't pay them any wages, and we pay ours wages but don't take care of them.

GOD:   Dixie isn't a popular tune, then?

BATTERED SOUL:   O, yes, very popular, very stirring, but you don't have to quit eating when a band plays it.

MARK TWAIN:   You see, if you get the people to worship a flag or a tune, they stop thinking and you can do anything with them.   Like making a king holy, kneeling to him, and then taking off your hat to his robe—then dying for him—the people—dung.   They kiss a king's nightshirt or a flag.

RABELAIS (*Aside*):   The Pope's toe.

GOD:   I see.   Idolatry.   Every time I examine your friends, my son, they make me tired.   Take this collision away and re-assemble it. Help him, Gabriel. A flag that really means freedom, in truth and fact, does not need any force to protect it, nor any rituals.   All idolatry is vicious.

(JESUS *and* GABRIEL *carry out the* BATTERED SOUL.)

RABELAIS:   *Mon ami,* isn't that United States the country where you are by law forbidden to drink wine?

INGERSOLL:   Yes.   Or think fine.   Its motto is P. P. P.

RABELAIS:   What does P. P. P. mean?

INGERSOLL:   Patriotism, prohibition, police.

RABELAIS:   Prohibition of what?

INGERSOLL:   Everything.   It is the triumph of mediocrity.   Rule by the fanatical minority.

RABELAIS:   And this patriotism?

VOLTAIRE:   *Cher ami,* you know bird-breeders set mechanical devices to whistle the tunes they wish their birds to sing in their cages.

RABELAIS:   Deceiving them with notes of liberty. Unhappy little victims.   Ignorant of skies.

VOLTAIRE:   *Voila*.   That is patriotism.   The tunes of the masters, taught to the birds in their cages.

(SAM JOHNSON *bustles in.*)

JOHNSON:   What's that?   What's that?   Patriotism?   The last refuge of scoundrels.   I said so long ago, didn't I, Bozzy?   Where is Boswell?

BOSWELL:   Here, Doctor.

JOHNSON:   Did I not say, sir, years ago, referring to the cloak with which our lords and political gamesters covered their exploitation of a deluded people, that patriotism is the last refuge of scoundrels?   Did I, or did I not?

BOSWELL:   You did, Doctor.   You did.

JOHNSON:   And I repeat it, sir.   I will hear no contradiction.   Show me patriotism and there I will show you trade exploitation hiding its bestial head.   Hiding, sir.   But the man of intellect can uncover him.

GOD:   Have you any men of intellect on earth, my son?   (*All are silent.*)   Ah, my son, the end is certain. The patriotism, the wars of your little animals will destroy them.   It will not take a million years.   Once more an imperial conquering exploiting nation goes to its death.

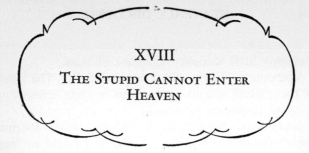

# XVIII
## The Stupid Cannot Enter Heaven

(*At the outer earthly gate of heaven. Beyond the gate, far as the eye can see, an infinite ocean of souls, clamoring to enter. Inside the gate* St. Peter *stands, surrounded by angels, gesticulating excitedly. Various souls gather*—Voltaire, Bruno, Shakespeare *and others.*

St. Peter: There is no use talking. Not one shall enter. Not one. God has issued his new decree. The Stupid Shall Not Enter the Kingdom of Heaven.

Gabriel: Do you mean to call all these millions and millions of souls stupid? English, German, French, Russian, Italian, Bulgarian, Serbian, Austrian, Hungarian, Americans—all?

St. Peter: Yes, all. Stupid in living; more stupid in their dying.

Luther: *Gott im Himmel.* Not the Germans. They died for Kaiser and fatherland.

Gabriel: Bigot. Yourself a rebel against churchly tyranny, yet preaching hell for rebels against temporal tyranny; pronouncing blessed any hand which should stab or poison the poor rebel peasants, hunger-stung to revolt against their lords. Heaven is now only for rebels. Go up to God. Make your peace with him. (Luther *goes out.*) No soul shall enter heaven who has oppressed the poor, or stolen their inheritance, and none who has submitted. Both are stupid.

VOLTAIRE: *Parbleu!* How crowded hell will be.

ST. PETER: Hell is abolished.

VOLTAIRE: Ah, yes, technically. Perhaps I should say how roomy heaven will be.

ST. PETER: I shall sleep at my gate.

VOLTAIRE: You will be a model concierge. But these poor devils must go somewhere.

ST. PETER: Back to earth. They must be born again.

VOLTAIRE: Ha! Not so bad.

GABRIEL: The Russian section is raising an awful row. They say they were promised heaven if they died in battle.

VOLTAIRE: Heaven through hell. The old cheap swindle.

ST. PETER: Who promised?

GABRIEL: The Czar; the Metropolitan; the nobles; the priests.

ST. PETER (*Interrupting*): They believed the promises of those who were riding on their backs. Tell them for this stupidity they must go to hell—I mean back to earth.

(GABRIEL *goes upon the battlement, sounds a parley, and announces* PETER'S *message.*)

VOLTAIRE: Heaven, what a howling those poor Russians set up. Like their own wolves. I am sorry for my dear, good friends, the generals and the aristocrats, the priests and the masters, when these souls get back into stout bodies with heads on them. Ah— with heads on them. Dear, dear. I wonder when it will happen.

SAVONAROLA: The Italians say the same thing.

GOD ISSUES A DECREE: "THE STUPID SHALL NOT ENTER HEAVEN."

They were promised for their loyalty, patriotism——

ST. PETER (*Interrupting*):  Didn't you hear me say to even believe that nonsense is enough to bar them out?  Stupidity now is the chiefest crime.

SAVONAROLA:  I shall intercede for them at the Throne of Infinite Pity.

ST. PETER:  Useless.  It is now the Throne of Pitiless Pity.  Moreover, Bruno is the head of the Italian Section.  Where is Bruno?

BRUNO:  Here I am.

ST. PETER:  You are head of the Italian angels. Heaven is now to be a place for thinkers.

VOLTAIRE:  Heavenly real estate will surely fall.

BRUNO:  Ah!  But if we deeply think, what will become of heaven itself?

ST. PETER:  Those are the orders.

BRUNO:  Ah, yes.  I see.  Thought will make a larger heaven.

VOLTAIRE:  It will surely be large enough.  One will journey far to gossip with a neighbor.  Like a night moth on a star, feeling into infinite space with its antennae.

ST. PETER:  Gabriel, what is that roaring?

GABRIEL:  It is the English souls.  They say if you don't let them in they are going to storm the walls; that they died fighting for Old England, and many sang "God Save the King" with their last breath.

ST. PETER:  God save—isn't that like the stupid English.  They died for that?    Well, they cannot come in.

GABRIEL:  They will storm the walls.

SHAKESPEARE:  And close the walls up with their English dead.

BEN JONSON: Bunk! Always there have been fools. Always will be. Close the walls up—why? What for? For whom? Bunk!

JACK CADE: I was nearer right than any of you. Fight for "Old England"? I said you mean "Old Lady of Threadneedle Street."

SHAKESPEARE: They laid the summer's dust with showers of blood raised from the wounds of slaughtered Englishmen.

BEN JONSON: Bunk! But yet the pity of it, Will. O, Will, the pity of it.

JACK CADE: For the masters. "God Save the King." I say God damn all kings.

ANTHONY COMSTOCK: St. Peter, Jack Cade swore. He said "God damn."

ST. PETER: It was a prayer. Your fig-leaf is torn.

ANTHONY COMSTOCK: Excuse me. Have you a thread and needle?

ST. PETER: Why don't you give up that disgusting fig-leaf habit?

VOLTAIRE: Don't rob him of his obscene pleasure.

ANTHONY COMSTOCK: Infidel.

VOLTAIRE: Thanks. Wear a thistle.

(ANTHONY goes out, holding his hands on his fig-leaf.)

What is he doing now?

ST. PETER: Growing fig-trees over in the irrigated districts reclaimed from hell.

VOLTAIRE: For the fruit?

ST. PETER: No, the leaves.

VOLTAIRE: Isn't he ashamed of the naked rocks?

ST. PETER: A little quiet, please. I cannot hear you all at once. What is it, Gabriel?

GABRIEL: The Frenchmen. They say there must be some mistake. Can one of their number come in as an envoy?

ST. PETER: O, very well, but only as an envoy. And it must not be a precedent.

(GABRIEL *goes out.*)

VOLTAIRE: You will never get him out again.

(GABRIEL *comes in with a* FRENCH SOUL.)

FRENCH SOUL: This, then, is God. (*Kneels to* ST. PETER.)

ST. PETER: Do not kneel. Here all are equal. Here is real freedom. I am not God, but Peter.

FRENCH SOUL: Ah! The greatest of the saints. I have heard of you, *Monseigneur.* I thought from your look you were God. You are the great St. Peter, Keeper of the Keys.

ST. PETER: What do you wish?

FRENCH SOUL: Ah, yes. I fear there is a misunderstanding somewhere; here or on earth.

ST. PETER: Very probably; but not here.

FRENCH SOUL: But by the infinite goodness and beauty of your countenance, I know we may expect justice.

VOLTAIRE (*Aside*): Delightful.

FRENCH SOUL: Outside there are some millions of us who died at Ypres, the Marne, the Somme, the Aisne, Verdun and a thousand little obscure holes and ditches, for *la belle France.*

ST. PETER: Be more definite. What is *la belle France?*

FRENCH SOUL: Oh, just *la belle France.* You understand. *La belle France.* Ah, *ma belle France.* (*Shrugs his shoulders.*)

(ALEXANDRE DUMAS PÈRE *comes up.*)

ALEXANDRE DUMAS PÈRE (*To* VOLTAIRE, *aside*): *Hola, Marie.*

VOLTAIRE (*To* DUMAS, *aside*): *Hola, Alexandre.*

ST. PETER: Do you mean the soil of France? Her valleys, mountains, rivers; her vineyards, olive-groves, fields, silk-mills, gun-factories, cities, banks, railroads, ships, forests, and mines?

FRENCH SOUL: Ah, such intelligence. Exactly.

ST. PETER: And how much of this was yours—yours and the others who died?

FRENCH SOUL: How much?

ST. PETER: Yes, how much?—Yours and the millions who died. How much of fatherland was the share of the German millions who died? What is your quarrel with one another? What do you get out of this, you millions who die? For what are you fighting each other?

VOLTAIRE (*To* DUMAS, *aside*): Delightful, Alexandre.

DUMAS (*To* VOLTAIRE, *aside*): Clever Jew.

FRENCH SOUL: But I do not understand. La belle France is where we lived.

ST. PETER: Yes? And fatherland is where the Germans lived. Was there not enough? What was the quarrel?

FRENCH SOUL: O, no quarrel—but patriotism, you know.

ST. PETER: You positively cannot come in. Too stupid. Where did you live in la belle France?

FRENCH SOUL: In Paris.

VOLTAIRE (*Aside*): Happy man.

ST. PETER: And how much of Paris was yours?

FRENCH SOUL: Well—the street.

DUMAS:   Ah, the streets of Paris!

ST. PETER:   The streets?

FRENCH SOUL:   Yes.  And that is the point.  I was an illegitimate waif, spewed out of the slums upon the streets of Paris.  They were my inheritance.  I became *gamin*; thief.

VOLTAIRE:   What did you steal?  Railways; domains; banks; mines?

FRENCH SOUL:   I do not understand, *Monsieur*. One cannot steal those.

VOLTAIRE:   True.  Only by law and consent of the stupid.

ST. PETER (*Aside*):   He is too stupid for the new heaven.

FRENCH SOUL:   I snatched ladies' purses, picked pockets.

VOLTAIRE (*Aside*):   He was the thief criminal, not the thief legal.

FRENCH SOUL:   I lured strangers, and so progressed, till by my industry and the help of a clever girl I had my own gambling establishment, my *objets de vertu*, my wine-cellar; my other mistresses.

VOLTAIRE (*Aside*):   Why be killed?

FRENCH SOUL:   But always I was promised hell by the *abbés* and good people who frequented my place.

VOLTAIRE:   Naturally.  Hell for him; heaven for them.

FRENCH SOUL:   I had illegitimate children by several mothers.

DUMAS:   Naturally.

VOLTAIRE:   Natural children.  Naturally.

FRENCH SOUL:   Then all was changed.  Those pigs, the Huns.

ST. PETER:  Who?

FRENCH SOUL:  The Huns—*Boches*—the German people.

ST. PETER:  Who?

FRENCH SOUL:  The German——

ST. PETER:  Rulers?

FRENCH SOUL:  Well, of course—the Germans made war on the French people.

ST. PETER:  On whom?

FRENCH SOUL:  On the French——

ST. PETER:  Masters?

FRENCH SOUL:  I don't know.  They said it was against all of us; and then we were promised if we fought for France all the illegitimates would be forgiven.  That meant much to me.  And we might get as many more as we could.  In fact, it would be our patriotic duty to do so—and all our crimes would be forgotten.

DUMAS:  That meant much also.

> Malbrouck S'en va-t-en guerre.
> Mironton—Mironton—Mirataine.

FRENCH SOUL:  That all our sins would be forgiven and the blackest cut-throat or gambler of us would go to heaven before any *abbé* or statesman or minister.

VOLTAIRE:  Very probable.

ST. PETER:  Who promised this?

FRENCH SOUL:  Everybody, *Monseigneur*.  The Church; the State; the President; the Press; even *Le Rire*.

VOLTAIRE:  It was its joke.  *Mon Dieu*, could you not see the humor of it?

FRENCH SOUL:  The clergy, Catholic and non-Catholic.  The poets.

St. Peter:  Did the poets promise that?

French Soul:  Oh, more.  They promised eternal fame.

Voltaire (*Aside*):  Ah, the poets!  What imagination!

French Soul:  The women kissed us and told us to be brave to die.

St. Peter:  For what?

Voltaire:  So that others might kiss.

Dumas:  Clever nymphs.

French Soul:  For *la patrie*.

St. Peter:  And that is what?

French Soul:  *O, Monseigneur!*

St. Peter:  Yes, I must get your idea.  I must know just why you wanted the Germans to kill you.

French Soul:  But, *Monseigneur,* we did not want the Germans to kill us.  We hoped to kill them.

St. Peter:  It is the same thing.  You hoped to kill them.  They hoped to kill you.  You cannot come in here if you have died stupidly, and everything you have said thus far is very stupid.

Voltaire:  It is.  Really it is, *mon ami.*  (*Aside*) Alexandre, do you not long for a game of *écarte?*

Dumas (*Aside*):  But yes.  Presently.  Wait a minute.  I have an idea.

St. Peter:  You and your fellows have died very stupidly.  You have been deceived.

French Soul:  Is it all a lie?

St. Peter:  Yes, all a lie.

French Soul:  *La patrie, l'honneur,* eternal fame, heaven?  All of it?

St. Peter:  All a lie, my poor soul.  All false.  You are a victim.  You must go now.  But you shall have

another chance.   You shall be born again and return
to Paris.

DUMAS:   Return to Paris?

ST. PETER:   Yes.

DUMAS:   Excuse me.   Allow me, good Peter.   My
good soul, I am your compatriot, Alexandre Dumas
*Père*.   I have been here now some little time.   I am
generous.   I will take your place.   You shall remain.
Good St. Peter, I will be his substitute.

ST. PETER:   You will surrender heaven to return to
Paris?

DUMAS:   *Hélas.*   Yes.   I will sacrifice myself.

ST. PETER:   Very well.   Go.

VOLTAIRE (*Aside*):   Clever rascal.

ST PETER (*To* FRENCH SOUL):   You may remain.
(*To Dumas*)   Alexandre, when next you die, see
that it be not stupidly.

DUMAS:   Trust me.   I shall know for what I die,
for whom I die, and why I die.   Ah, my dear Peter.
If you knew how this parting wrings my heart.   In
our comparatively brief acquaintance I have become so
attached to you, though we have had our little differ-
ences.   Forgive my emotion.

VOLTAIRE:   I will take your place, Alexandre.   You
shall not make this sacrifice.

DUMAS:   No, no, kind friend.   *Au revoir.*   Dear
Peter, *au revoir*.

(DUMAS *hastens out.*)

VOLTAIRE:   Paris.   *Hélas!*   Lucky fellow.   Heaven,
what an uproar!

ST. PETER:   Gabriel, go tell them it is useless.   They
must go away and try to die more intelligently next
time.

(GABRIEL *sounds a parley from the battlements and*

*makes the proclamation.   There is a bedlam of shrieks,*
*cries,   and   exclamations   "Deceived—deceived—de-*
*ceived."*)

GABRIEL:   They won't go.   They say "Where shall
we go?   We'd rather go to hell than back to earth
while this war is on."

ST. PETER:   Hell is abolished.

VOLTAIRE (*Aside*):   Old style.

ST. PETER:   They must go.   It is the decree.

GABRIEL:   The Poles say they were promised nothing; just slaughtered; first by Russians, then by Germans and Austrians.   Then again by Russians.   Their
country harried; their crops destroyed; their cattle
taken and hundreds of thousands of babies starved to
death.   There is not a child under seven in the land.
The race risks extinction.   England will not let relief
come in.   Germany will not permit aid.

SHAKESPEARE (*Aside*):   And these be Christians.

GABRIEL:   They are caught between the upper and
nether millstone, helpless between two great armies.

ST. PETER:   Let them come in.   Place guards.   Let
none but Poles enter.   The others positively must die
again.

(GOD *is on his throne*. VOLTAIRE, RABELAIS, IN-
GERSOLL, *and others are near the throne*.)

(ST. PETER, GABRIEL, RAPHAEL, *the* DEVIL, *and a
host rush in, panic-stricken*.)

ST. PETER: Save yourself, Lord. Save yourself.
Something has got in.

GABRIEL: It broke down the gate.

RAPHAEL: It is coming. Save yourself.

GOD: Is it the Devil?

SATAN: No, no. I am here. Hide me. Omnipotence, I ask protection.

GOD: Who is it?

INGERSOLL: What a roaring.

VOLTAIRE (*To* RABELAIS): My friend, I guess
heaven has come to an end.

RABELAIS: That does not trouble me.

SATAN: O, that roar. Hide me. I never thought
he'd get in here. Hide me. I know him.

GOD: Who is this thing of terror?

SATAN: Yes. That's him. T. R. T. R. Don't
you know him? T. R.? (SATAN'S *teeth chatter*.)

GOD: Never heard of him.

SATAN: Never heard of Teddy? O, God!

GOD: No, I never heard of him. Stop shivering.

SATAN:   Oh! Oh! Surely you know the Colonel.

GOD:   Never heard of him, I tell you.   But what a frightful uproar.   Is it an army?

ST. PETER:   No.   Just him.   Just him.   But, O, God——

(*Enter T. R.   He holds out his hand to God.*)

T. R.:   Dee-lighted.   Dee-lighted, I am sure.   I have heard of you.

GOD:   Indeed.

T. R.:   Possibly we have met somewhere?

GOD:   No, I think not.

T. R.:   Were you ever in Washington, D. C.?

GOD:   Never.

T. R.:   Well, there is certainly something familiar about you.   Don't rise.

GOD:   Take my seat.

T. R.:   Thanks awfully.   (*Sits down.*)   Now, where is Michael?

GOD:   He is away in a new star called the Orb of Brotherly Love.

T. R.:   Why, that's our earth.

GOD:   No.   This is different.

T. R.:   Well, who is commander-in-chief here?   It drives me crazy to sit quiet this way.   Who is commander-in-chief?

GOD:   We have no commander-in-chief.

T. R.:   Who leads your armies?

GOD:   We have no armies.

T. R.:   What?   No armies?   I don't believe it. How do you get on?   How will you defend yourself? Well, who is head of your organization?

GOD:   We have no organization.

T. R.:   No organization?   No armies?   Well, it's a mighty good thing I came.   How on earth—I mean,

how in heaven—are you going to get into this war without an army, and how are you going to levy taxes and
conscript the angels without an organization?

GOD:   But we are not going into any war.

T. R.:   Not going into the war!   Do you seriously
tell me that you are not going into this great war to
end war and for freedom and democracy and world
peace?   Have I died in vain only to come to a heaven
of cowards, dastards, poltroons, contemptible, white-
livered, white-feathered, chicken-hearted slackers.
Have you no patriotism, no sense of national honor,
dignity or democracy?   Have you no common brotherhood, no Christian unity?

(GABRIEL *and the* BATTERED SOUL OF THE PACIFIST
*enter.   The* BATTERED SOUL *has been put together, but
wobbles in spots.*)   Listen to me.   You certainly are
going into this war.   I'll raise a division myself or I'll
raise hell and I'll show you what the fighting spirit is.
We are going into this war.   Do you understand?

VOLTAIRE:   *Voila les dents.*

RABELAIS:   *Sang de Dieu.*

T. R. ( *To* GABRIEL):   What is your name?

GABRIEL:   My name is Gabriel.

T. R.:   O, yes, Gabriel; trumpeter.   I remember.
Dee-lighted, I am sure.   Go out at once and organize a publicity bureau.   Make a proclamation that a
T. R. Club must be started in every precinct.   Re-
cruiting offices must be opened all over heaven.   Proclaim and also post notices that Colonel Roosevelt will
in person lead an army of angels against the Huns in
the great cause of Christianity and democracy, and ex-
pects every angel with a drop of red blood in his veins
to volunteer, and if any dirty, sneaking, white-feathered slacker refuses to do his bit—(*the* BATTERED SOUL

*falls into a fit*). Well, well. What's the matter here?

GABRIEL: This poor Battered Soul has just fallen in a fit.

GOD: Revive him.

(BATTERED SOUL *revives and* GABRIEL *lifts him up.*) What is the matter?

BATTERED SOUL: O, dear God, every time I hear those words I fall in a fit.

GOD: What words?

BATTERED SOUL: "Do his bit."

GOD: But you can't afford to fall in a fit for all the silly words you hear.

T. R.: Silly! Silly! Those modest, beautiful, patriotic, eloquent, noble words silly? I tell you that every man must either do his country, his bit, or somebody. Gabriel, have all the white-winged angels dyed red, white, and blue—no, red and blue. I won't have a white-feathered one in my whole army. Make 'em red. No, not red—that's Bolshevik. Make 'em blue— I don't like it, but it can't be helped. Make 'em blue.

GABRIEL: My commands come from God.

T. R.: Sure. Don't you hear me? I'm going to take over to Germany—yes, to the whole world, to the whole universe, my honor, my patriotism, my loyalty, my policies, my democracy, my Christianity, myself.

VOLTAIRE: *Ciel! les dents.*

RABELAIS: *La voix.*

VOLTAIRE: Might I humbly suggest it has been brought to us here that the Germans claim a world *Kultur* and a democracy also? Indeed, as I look down upon them, it seems to me if they would only unhorse their spurred riders, they have the foundation for a better society than yours: no slums; no poverty; no hopeless old age.

T. R.: I'll unhorse their spurred riders for them.

VOLTAIRE: Perhaps. But don't you think every people should unhorse its own riders? A revolution from the outside? No, impossible. A people must make its own revolution.

T. R.: Sir, I tell you I shall annihilate them. What the world needs is the democracy of America, of New York, of Ludlow, of Paterson, of Lawrence, of Bayonne, of Passaic, of the Solid South, united with the splendid democracy of England, of Ireland, of India, of Africa, of Egypt. I shall annihilate this German militarism with a more thorough militarism of my own.

RABELAIS: *Pardon. Pardon, Monsieur.* Spare something. In the name of the gullet, if not of Christianity, spare the delicious Strasbourg paté; the leberwurst; the Westphalia hams. Ah, those excellent Westphalian thirst-provokers. Spare the Bismarck herring; kielerspratten, sardellen, sausages. Heaven, the sausages, with rye bread—the bread of the people, and beer —the drink of the people: pale amber Pilsner and dark, topaz Münchner. Slayers of throat-parching thirsts; one envies the giraffe his neck. Beer, the liquid bread of the ancient Egyptians; foaming nectar, smelling of the Bohemian hop-yards where the sun shines in September on festooned vines; the air aromatic with golden pollen blown from the pendant hops. Jewels on the neck of a tall, blonde, voluptuous Gretchen. Hops are medicinal, sir. A golden gift from golden-crowned Ceres. Medicinal. I am a physician and tell you so. I beg you spare beer. And do not speak of annihilating the golden sweat from those sunny slopes of the Rhine, the Moselle. O, the long-necked bottles of liquid sunshine, gift of the antique twisted vines, centuries rooted in good German soil. Johannesberger,

Steinberger, Hochheimer, Liebfraunmilch—are we not poetical under our arbor? The milk of Venus. And our good Doctor Berncastler. The Steinwein, Riesling and Weisling. Not bottled drunkenness and combat, sir, but bottled friendship, good comradeship, songs, handclasps, weddings, christenings, feastings, the sap of good old Mother Earth. The sacrament of love and brotherhood. Yes, sir, and of religion. The golden blood of the great Dionysus. O, those oaken tuns of the Rhine. I, a Frenchman, sir, would hasten peace and return to earth if I might lie under their aureate shower. Spare something of Germany, sir. And there is music and medicine, science and drama, and blonde Gretchens, sir. I, a Frenchman, plead that you leave us something of Germany.

T. R.: Who are you?

RABELAIS: *Pardon, Monsieur.* François Rabelais. Let me say with proud humility, one of the makers of France.

T. R.: O, I know you; an obscene old drunkard.

RABELAIS: *Pardon.* A humorist. Never drunk, except with my own fancies.

T. R.: A lecherous old scoundrel.

RABELAIS: *Pardon encore.* Never lecherous. All merely humor. Scoundrel—Ah—*peut-être—chacun à son gout.*

T. R.: I say you are obscene.

RABELAIS: *Hélas,* there is nothing so obscene as war.

T. R.: You are a drunkard.

RABELAIS: *Ma foi.* Are you perhaps also a humorist? There is no drunkenness like to war; nothing so foolish—so useless. What has it ever settled? What has it ever brought that was worth the price? The supreme stupidity of man is war—the game whose pawns are the young men. When did ever a people make war? When did ever a people want war till they were first made drunken by the masters? War, the supreme stupidity; the drunkenness of all drunkenness!

T. R.: I, myself, am temperate in all things.

RABELAIS: In *all* things? In *all* things?

T. R.: Yes, sir; in all things and at all times.

GOD: How we deceive ourselves. (*To* GABRIEL, *who leads* T. R. *away*.) Gabriel, let him look at Alexander, Hannibal, Caesar, Napoleon, the great soldiers who each and all made a failure of fighting.

(SATAN *comes out from his hiding behind* GOD *and* ST. PETER. JESUS *comes in*.)

SATAN: I breathe again.

GOD: Let us all meditate in the hush of this sudden quiet, invoking from the universe—peace. Peace, the great builder; the great healer; the plow that turns the furrows of civilization for the rain of love.

JESUS: Unless this come the peoples shall surely perish.

## XX

### PRINCE BUTTINSKY

(GOD *is tossing up a baby angel and catching her.*
INGERSOLL, VOLTAIRE, RABELAIS *talk together.*)

INGERSOLL:   It looks to me as if more trouble was
coming.   This reminds me of getting the returns elec-
tion night.

(ST. PETER *comes in with* ELIHU ROOT.)

(GOD *puts down the baby angel.*)

GOD:   Run along.   Run along now.   What day is
this?

INGERSOLL:   Friday.

GOD:   Thank myself, tomorrow will be a half holiday.

INGERSOLL:   Yes, and the next day Sunday.

GOD:   More grief for me.   Prayers.   O the prayers.
How they smell.   You would think I was a bad actor.
Well, what is it now?   (*To* ST. PETER, *who mops his
brow with the tail of his robe.*)

ST. PETER:   Excuse me; I am all out of breath.   This
soul got in while the gate was down.   (*Points to soul
of* ELIHU ROOT.)

GOD:   Have you fixed it?

ST. PETER:   Just patched it.   That boisterous, bel-
ligerent, bellowing soul, T. R., knocked it so to pieces
I am afraid we'll have to call in that pagan blacksmith.

GOD:   Vulcan?

St. Peter: Yes.

God: O, leave it down.

St. Peter: You forget this earth war and your new law that none of the stupid shall inherit heaven.

God: Very well; let Vulcan fix it. (*To the soul of* Elihu Root.) Now, who are you?

Elihu Root: I am Prince Buttinsky, head of the Buttinsky Commission.

God: Are you a Russian?

Elihu Root: Well, not exactly; only partly. You see, it's like this——

Ingersoll: Aren't you my old friend, Elihu Root?

Elihu Root: That was my name, but I went to Russia on a commission and over there they called it the Rootoff Commission and gave me the name of Prince Buttinsky.

God: What was your commission?

Elihu Root: Well, you see I and some other socialists——

Ingersoll: Socialists? What socialists?

Elihu Root: Charles Edward Russell, English Walling, John Spargo——

Ingersoll: Socialists?

Elihu Root: We went to Russia after the Russian revolution to take to those poor, benighted people some of our liberty and democracy, canned.

Voltaire: *Nom de Dieu.*

Elihu Root: The United States has the greatest democracy on earth. Every peaceable individual is free to do exactly as he likes, as long as he doesn't interfere with others. Free speech is absolute. Anyone can express any opinion at any time, in war or peace. There is no master class, and no wage-slaves. No tyranny; no dependents; no slums; no poverty.

The natural resources of the country are held by and used for the whole people.   There are no special privileges, but perfect equality of opportunity, and the only aristocracy is that of mind and soul.   No discontent; no strikes.   No militarism.   All are happy and contented, and all are absolutely free in body, thought, speech, and soul.   Perfect tolerance, perfect freedom.

INGERSOLL:   Whew!

RABELAIS (*To* VOLTAIRE):   Where is that place?

VOLTAIRE:   I do not know.

INGERSOLL:   Root, when I left the United States there was just this much freedom: the few were free to exploit the country and the people, and the people were free to hunt jobs and work, and a man was free to speak so long as he did not say anything offensive to the ruling class.   Nero's freedom.

ELIHU ROOT:   Don't you believe in the survival of the fittest?

INGERSOLL:   A pirate is not always the fittest.

GOD:   Go on, Prince.

ELIHU ROOT:   In Russia they had no liberty. Everything was under a spy system.   Arbitrary arrests. Censorships of everything.   Billions of taxes.   The police were nothing but agents of the government, keeping down freedom of speech.   Even the courts did the will of the government.   The post office suppressed mail.   It was a bureaucratic tyranny, so we thought we would take our system over to them.

GOD:   Where is that Battered Soul?

BATTERED SOUL:   Here I am.

GOD:   Tell Prince Buttinsky about your land of freedom.

BATTERED SOUL:   I was beaten to pulp because I

didn't rise when the band played the "Star Spangled Banner."

ELIHU ROOT: Certainly. We must have patriotism or we couldn't have war—war to save the world.

BATTERED SOUL: I thought I had a right to sit still —just peaceably and quietly sit still.

ELIHU ROOT: There you are. Why, this man wanted to sit still when the majority got up. He wanted to oppose his opinion to the will of the mob— majority, I mean. He was a traitor to his country, land of the free.

INGERSOLL: I am proud of my country's self-sacrifice. It Prussianizes itself that it may un-Prussianize Germany and Russianizes itself that it may un-Russianize Russia. That it may carry self-government to the world, it destroys what little self-government it had.

(GOD *is left alone, contemplating some mosses.*)

GOD: Mosses from the earth. Well, at least there is some good on that ball. I am glad I made these.

(GOD *is standing on the grand terrace of the first
eternity, curiously examining a baby star.*)

GOD:    Gabriel.

GABRIEL:    Yes, Lord.

GOD:    Where is the Devil?

GABRIEL:    On earth.

GOD:    What earth?

GABRIEL:    Jesus' earth.

GOD:    O, that pestiferous pill.  What is he doing?

GABRIEL:    Raising hell.

GOD:    How?

GABRIEL:    The war, you know. Killing men; starving babies; outraging women.  General destruction.
Then there is the United States.  He just loves it.  Says
it has a great future.

GOD:    For him or for Jesus?

GABRIEL:    O, for him.

GOD:    Call Jesus.

(GABRIEL *goes out.*  JESUS *comes in.*)

My son, why do you care so much for the earth?
It is insignificant in size, gives no light, no warmth.
Do you care for the little ball, or for the animals on it?

JESUS:    For man, Father.

GOD:    Why do you select man?  The other animals
are more dignified.  I'll tell you why I ask.  I am think-

ing that instead of allowing man to slowly blot himself out, I may destroy the whole ball to get rid of him at once.

JESUS:   O, no Father.

GOD:   Why not?  Here is a new star which I am going to set whirling; pure, perfect, luminous; not a living thing on it, just a pearl for the deeps of space. It is peaceful, beautiful, serene, and will sing in harmony as it flies.   Suppose it had your swarm of petty, fellow-destroying, self-destroying, fellow-devouring, self-devouring, fellow-persecuting, self-persecuting, stupid, besotted cannibal bugs on it.   Don't you see what a blot it would be in the universe?   Instead of joyfully whirling it off into space I would blot it out. Why not your earth?

JESUS:   Because, Father, remember not what men are but what they were.   Atoms.   Remembering what they were, think what they may become.   I have hopes that in some millions of years I will see them civilized, all at peace with each other; intercourse and trade all free with each other; a happy human family: their great ambition not to rule and rob each other, but each to contribute his part in things and in soul to the general good, secure in a mutual happiness; knowing that each one's highest happiness is only to be found when all are happy.

GOD:   You are always the optimist.

JESUS:   Yes.   I hope they will some day learn that self-seeking leads to destruction; that not charity, but Love the mother of Justice is the cure.   The whole planet one great common inheritance, the rivalry among them to be to maintain a perfect freedom in a perfect peace.   All the resources of earth belonging to all in a friendly free exchange; no cut-throat competition any-

where, and the exploitation of fellow beings or the un-
just accumulation of a superfluity of things a disgrace:
mere ownership of things, without spiritual performance, a failure.   Life a poem as earth and cosmos are
poetry.

GOD:   When is this to be?

JESUS:   You promised me a million years.

GOD:   Ah, so soon?  For you, dear son, there should
be a stronger word than optimist.

JESUS:   Eternity is long, Father.  The earth has en-
dured but the twinkling of an eye.

GOD:   I have sent for the Devil to hear what he has
to say.   Earth is his chief playground and I ought to
consider him.   I am an anarchist.   It seems to me, my
son, he outruns you in the race.

JESUS:   O Father, do you believe it is really so?

GOD:   There is another who has distanced you—
taken your mantle and turned it wrong side out.

JESUS:   Who?

GOD:   Saul, who Romanized himself into Paul, the
great Roman organizer, who organized you into an institution.

JESUS:   Yes, father.   Dear, earnest, eloquent Saul
did not understand me.   But he was devoted and sincere—he died for his faith.

GOD:   No, he did not understand you.   You were
the poet, the dreamer.   But he understood men.   He
understood that power lay with organization and property.   Thinking to help your socialistic fight for the
exploited against the exploiters, he joined your church
to power and to property, and so to spiritual death. He
made your ministers preach content, not agitation;
faith, not intellect; submission to authority, not each
free in his own soul; and his church, called Peter's, be-

came the most relentless authority on earth.   Again and again it has crucified the scientist, the poet, the dreamer, the agitator, the stirrer-up of the people even as you, the stirrer-up of the people, were crucified.

JESUS:   Here he comes now.

GOD:   I was just telling my son you betray him.  A worse enemy than Satan.  Satan stimulates; you crush and smother with authority, claiming heaven as your own.

PAUL:   I—I—betray my blessed Saviour—in whom I have redemption through his blood.  All things are under his feet and he is the head of the church.

GOD:   Head of *the* church as if there was only one church.  What need has my son of a worldly church with a powerful worldly head?  Did he preach such, seek such?  Saul, Saul, you have the gift of words, but they are sounding brass and a tinkling cymbal.  To you the church, an ambitious institution of property and political power, is more than the spirit that saves.  You exalt priests, degrade women, support the masters, prais-ing blind faith, damning man's free thought—wives submit, servants obey—take no thought of earth, hope for heaven—humility, servility.  Declaring kings and popes my son's agents.  Myself save the mark.  Popes and kings his agents!  Christ's agents.  Unthinkable! Making property sacred, more than flesh and blood. Form, form, form; ritual instead of truth and the spirit. Obedience instead of man's divine right to think for himself and to act as his own soul declares.  When did my son impose himself with authority and power and splendor and pride?  When did my son declare any authority but love and a free soul?  You have distorted my son's word, and made sacred a great machine of property and worldly power—the Church of Christ. Of Christ! Christ!

PAUL: Lord! Lord! Why persecutest thou me?

GOD: I never persecute but my truth works relentlessly.

JESUS: Paul, the truth shall set you free. Father, Paul erred honestly.

GOD: I know no honesty, only error.

JESUS: Here comes Satan.

GOD: Ah—now, at least we shall be stimulated.

(GABRIEL *and* SATAN *come in.*)

SATAN: Hail! Highness.

GOD: What should I say? Hail! Lowness.

SATAN: As you please, Omnipotence. Titles to me have become trifles.

GOD: Always sensible. What are you doing?

SATAN: Do you ask for information or for amusement?

GOD: Never mind why I ask. Answer.

SATAN: I desire to temper my answer to your mood. You should get down into life more. It soils perhaps, but is amusing. Heights are so lonely.

GOD: Are you never lonely?

SATAN: Not a minute.

GOD: And I am always lonely. Tell me where you are at work and what doing.

SATAN: I am working the earth. The war is now taking care of itself. Their Christian hatreds grow more bitter every day. Under my guidance the masters are lying to the people, through eye and ear, to inflame them to fear and hate. A "holy" war built on lies. A "war to end war" resting on hate, present and future. They strain every nerve to kill and torture each other for their masters. They laugh at babies' dying wails, set traps to mangle men, leave them to die horribly and go laughing off. Each calls the others fiends and makes new reprisals. For soldiers food is snatched from the mouths of mothers. The maimed, the halt, the blind strew the land, and all for the masters! And the harvest—O they do not see the harvest, but I see and laugh, laugh, laugh—centuries of suffering and tax paying; all for the masters. Conquest and exploitation by the masters, which will stir up new conquests, new exploitation, new wars. Christ's teaching has fallen from hypocritical shoulders like a rotten cloak snatched by the wind. They have their teeth in each other's throats and drink blood—for their masters, for their masters' Trade; their masters' Profit; their masters' Competition; masters against masters, and so, war. Jesus, I have not laughed so much since you were first crucified; folly, folly—the supreme folly. I work with the masters. We work together. Only let me whisper: "Your fat privileges are in danger." See them start up and with all the cruelty of terror, lay about them. Hangings, burnings, prisons, dungeons. And the churches of Jesus Christ gather up their skirts and hurry along with them. I fly to an island in the Caribbean and laugh till I can laugh no more. All the time each is praying to you, Omnipotence, for victory, and slaughtering in your name, Jesus.

JESUS: Whitened sepulchres. Within are dead men's bones and death.

SATAN: No, no, Jesus. Not hypocrites. Not at all —just self-conceit and greed. I laugh and laugh. Here are the poor wretches toiling, sweating—slaves, slaves, slaves. They grow desperate. They want a larger crust, and pitifully ask for bread, light, warmth, rest. Up start I and whisper to the masters: "Your profits are in danger—your privileges, by which you live on the people's backs." Then they sound alarms; call out the police. Jails and killings are in order, and Jesus' church joins in. Jesus, the crucified agitator—Jesus, the stirrer-up of the people. His church joins the hue and cry. I have one last word to conjure with: I shout "Anarchists"—and the whole world goes insane with stupid fear. Is it not laughable?

GOD: Truly laughable, and only possible with fools. I am myself an anarchist. Jesus is the supreme anarchist. The Golden Rule—the very creed of anarchism, and yet you see how stupid the people are. Better let me destroy them all.

SATAN: O, no, I join Jesus in begging you to stay your hand. Without Christians I would be without occupation.

GOD: Really, it is amusing. I can see Satan's side of it, my son. A lot of plain, hard-working slaves toiling for masters, and rushing at each other's throats to perpetuate their slavery—they having no quarrel, kill each other for the masters, and kill the saviours who would set them free. Is it not amusing?

JESUS: Brother, why do you drive my poor people mad?

SATAN: Who? I? They go crazy by stupidly swallowing stupid words. Old tricks. The same old bait always swallowed. The ancient monarchs used it—"Loyalty," and their people died for monarchy; "Patriotism," and their serfs died for slavery; "the King," "the Dynasty," "the System," "the Flag," "O the Flag!" and the miserable, downtrodden slaves die for a word, a falsity. Willingly, willingly they die shouting "Country," "Flag," "Honor," and such trick words of the masters. Why do you not laugh? In the wars of York and Lancaster, Englishmen killed Englishmen to settle which particular group of aristocrats should fatten on Englishmen. The Lords of York yelled "Patriotism," "Loyalty," "the Flag," and Yorkist slaves rushed merrily to die for Yorkist masters. The Lords of Lancaster yelled "Patriotism," "Loyalty," "the Flag" and Lancaster peasants rushed out to die for their favorite color. It is the same now: same words, same craze, same slaves, same slaughter, same cripples, same debts for the people to pay, same profits for the masters to take, same stupidity. Laugh Jesus. Laugh with me.

JESUS: The people of the United States are sane. You have not caught them.

SATAN: Excuse me while I smile! Have you heard your preacher Manning of New York shouting for blood and battle and military training?

JESUS: No minister of mine is preaching hate and bloodshed and the use of armies.

SATAN: O, you live up too high. Your servants are all with me. I'll have the United States in a week. The masters are mad now to join the carouse of blood, and when the masters are ready, the helpless sheep go to the slaughter.

JESUS: But why?

SATAN: Profits, Profits, Power, Places in the Sun, Trade, Greed. The people are already taking the bait "National Honor," "Patriotism," "Save the World from the other Fellow and for Us."

JESUS: But how will the slaughter of more millions decide even these questions?

SATAN: It won't. It will decide more wars. Wars breed wars, always.

Oho, it is a pretty game!
Blood, blood, blood in a flood.
A million blind, a million lame,
Babes and women without food,
Poor fools fighting for their masters—
Poor fools dying faster, faster,
All destruction!  All disaster!
And why?  Why?  Why?—
Hark!  I hear a woman cry.
Why, why should the people die?
No one can tell.
Laughter in hell.  Laughter in hell.

GOD:  Don't you really think, my son, that I had better blot out the earth?

JESUS:  You need not destroy the beautiful green planet to make an end of man.  He will destroy himself.

SATAN:  May I go?  They await me in the United States.

GOD:  Go.  Man must save himself if he be saved at all.

(SATAN *goes out.*)

JESUS:  Father, help me.  What is the trouble?

GOD:  Lack of brains; lack of education in truth and truth in education.  The instinct for self-preservation crushed.  When your animals have the sense to see that the private ownership of the great natural resources of the planet by a few and the great artificial privileges of the social organization produce continual poverty and unceasing war at home; when they see that war is only the ruling few of each country competing for exploitation of the world, just as at home they exploit the people, they will abolish this private ownership of the great planetary and social resources, and so will abolish poverty and war.  When each and all of them have brains to see that the self-interest of all is the self-interest of each, a world free trade will come—then wars will end and not till then.

JESUS:   Will the people not learn that love of others, justice to others, is true self-interest?

GOD:   First take the bone from between the hungry dogs.   Now watch me throw this beautiful, barren star! On it will rest peace.

(GOD *throws the star and* GOD *and* JESUS *watch the flight.*)

## XXII
### Satan Loses His Mind

(God *is resting in a cloud.* St. Peter *comes in.*)

St. Peter: O Omnipotence—Lord—God—Jehovah.

God: Well.

St. Peter: Satan is at the gate.

God: What does he want?

St. Peter: Only to speak with you.

God: Let him come in.

(St. Peter *goes out.* Rabelais, Voltaire, Bob Ingersoll, *the* Czar of Russia *comes in.*)

Voltaire: *Bon jour—Bon jour—Mon Seigneur.* Have you heard the news?

God: I hear all things.

Voltaire: Pardon—I, myself, am a little deaf. Then you know Satan has lost his mind?

God: What?

Voltaire: Satan has lost his mind.

God: Impossible. Like myself, he is eternal.

Rabelais: *Hélas!* What will the world do?

Voltaire: He began acting very queerly when Russia deposed our friend here.

The Czar: I—their Little Father. Yes. They deposed their Little Father.

Voltaire: Insolence.

Ingersoll: Their good Little Father.

RABELAIS:   Ah, Papa, Papa!  What would poor common clay do without its papas?

VOLTAIRE:   They deposed and executed Little Father and when the Russian soldiers refused to be slaughtered any more in the great war for peace, for brotherhood, for democracy, for the lesser peoples, etc., etc., Satan shunned the company of his best friends, the generals and statesmen, and went about muttering "Refuse to kill," "Refuse to be killed," "Brotherhood of the workers of the world," "O this is the end," "This is the end"; over and over he muttered "This is the end."

INGERSOLL:   Not yet.  Not by a long shot.  Watch the Workers of the World continue to kill each other by command of their masters.

VOLTAIRE:   When the Communism of Soviets was created he became sullen and relapsed into silence, in spite of what the other governments did for him.

THE CZAR:   My dear old friend—he was always loyal to me.

VOLTAIRE:   And when Germany offered to make peace on the Fourteen Points——

GOD:   On the what?

VOLTAIRE:   The Fourteen Points, Omniscience.

GOD:   Points of what?  Swords or theology?

INGERSOLL:   Neither, Omnipotence;  just points. You know a point is an imaginary thing having position but not dimension.

VOLTAIRE:   Pardon, Omniscience.  You who know all things surely know the Fourteen Points are——

GOD:   Yes, yes, I know—a schoolboy trick—tack-points in a chair.

RABELAIS:   A schoolmaster trick.  Fourteen pin points in a presidential chair.

VOLTAIRE: *Certainement*. You put your—ahem— your—what shall I say——

RABELAIS: Brains.

VOLTAIRE: Yes. Your brains in the chair and rise suddenly—the great surprise—the Fourteen Points.

INGERSOLL: They certainly were a great surprise.

PAINE: And disappointment.

THE CZAR: But inform me, please. Truly, what are these Fourteen Points?

INGERSOLL: O nothing—absolutely nothing.

VOLTAIRE: A sort of slang? *Argot?*

INGERSOLL: Thimble-rig. Now you see them and now you don't.

THE CZAR: Ah! A joke.

INGERSOLL: Exactly. The joke of the world.

VOLTAIRE: And, Omniscience—when peace was declared on the Fourteen Points——

THE CZAR: Peace? On the joke?

INGERSOLL: Yes. A joke on the joke.

RABELAIS: A joke on peace. Ha! I know. The Versailles Treaty.

INGERSOLL: Exactly.

VOLTAIRE: When peace was declared our friend sank into a settled melancholy.

INGERSOLL: How foolish.

PAINE: So shortsighted.

(SATAN *comes in, supported by* ST. PETER.)

RABELAIS: *Courage, courage, mon ami le diable!* Do you not know that dogs return to their—ah, that is to say make their lunch off their breakfast—and will deliciously roll in carrion? O interesting friend, be not so easily discouraged. Watch mankind. *Courage!* They will fight again.

VOLTAIRE: What! Is Satan, the shrewd, so foolish

as to expect peace among wolves, foxes, and tigers?

SATAN:   I prostrate myself before you, Mr. Wilson.

GOD:   What do you say, my friend?

SATAN:   I humble myself before you, Mr. Wilson.

GOD:   Wilson—Wilson—Who is this Wilson?

INGERSOLL:   He is the President of the United States. Earth.

GOD:   That earth—a flea—small but you cannot escape it.   So, he mistakes me for this Wilson?

INGERSOLL:   Yes, Omniscience—but Mr. Wilson himself often made the same mistake.

VOLTAIRE:   It is sad to see a great intellect in ruin.

INGERSOLL:   The mind that rules the world reduced to this.

VOLTAIRE:   A master mind, but he had his faults.

RABELAIS:   His faults were his virtue.

SATAN:   Mr. Wilson——

GOD:   Well—well. My poor friend, what do you want?

SATAN:   Let us have peace.   A peace without victory.   No punitive damages, and the lesser peoples——

GOD:   Poor fellow. How he rambles.   Take care of him—Let him have the Glittering Gallery to himself till he recovers.

JESUS:   I was going to ask you to let me go to Mars for my Easter vacation.

GOD:   Mars?

JESUS:   For peace and quiet. I could not spend this Easter on earth—but I will remain here and minister to this sufferer.   (JESUS *leads* SATAN *out*.)

GOD:   I thought him my worst enemy, but I see he was my best friend.   Let heaven wear mourning for a stellar cycle.

# XXIII

## God's Picnic

(*The Peak of Heavenly Peace.* God *is sitting on a campstool, viewing the cosmos. Near Him are* RABELAIS, VOLTAIRE, MARK TWAIN, BOB INGERSOLL, J. P. MORGAN, TOM PAINE, MARGARET FULLER, SAPPHO, *and* CARRIE NATION. HERMES *stands on the right of* GOD, *a little retired.*)

GOD:   Gabriel. Gabriel. Where is Gabriel?

HERMES:   During your picnic, Omniscience, he is on vacation.  I am on duty.

GOD:   Ah, yes.  Then I shall be well served, graceful sky-cleaver.  Tell Jesus I would like to speak with him.

HERMES:   Instantly, Ruler of Heaven.

(HERMES *goes out.*)

GOD:   By myself, it is good to be rid of all the formality, ritual and ceremony; the ages have weighted me with barnacles.  Here is simplicity—peace.  O those harpists from the earth.  I never could understand why the earth imagines I am so fond of their music, and always the harp.  Amateur harpists, aeon after aeon, each playing for himself.  O, by the way, Robert.

INGERSOLL:   Yes, Lord.

GOD:   I let Carrie Nation come to our picnic this time on your account.

INGERSOLL:   I am sorry for your thoughtlessness, Omniscience——

GOD: She said it would be heaven if she could just be near you, and this is heaven, you know.

INGERSOLL: I suppose so; for her. Did she bring her hatchet?

GOD: No. Of course not. I don't permit any conversions by force.

INGERSOLL: Then you are not a prohibitionist.

GOD: Robert, I prohibit nothing. I leave men free.

INGERSOLL: Carrie is trying to get George Washington to organize the Noble Order of the Hatchet.

GOD: Where did you hear that?

INGERSOLL: George told me. She wants him to be the Past Grand Exalted Handle.

GOD: Ah.

INGERSOLL: She is to be the High Immaculate Edge.

GOD: Well, let them. This is heaven.

INGERSOLL: Why not let her join Peter? He has a great organization.

GOD: I didn't bring Peter this time. I found he and Paul were trying to organize, institutionalize, and ritualize even these picnics, taking all the fun out of them.

INGERSOLL: Well, he'll enjoy being in charge during your absence.

GOD: He isn't in charge. I left Buddha in charge. He is very tolerant. Call your friends over here.

(INGERSOLL *beckons and the others approach.*)
Ladies and gentlemen, what were you discussing? Something very interesting, no doubt.

MARK TWAIN: Not very—Man.

GOD: Even a microbe may be interesting.

MARK TWAIN: Certainly. A microbe has no pretense, no egotism, no cruelty, no ignorance, no stupidity, no vanity; a microbe attends to its own business.

MARGARET FULLER: We were wondering why men are so determined each to be free for himself, each to live his own life, yet so insistent to interfere with the lives of others.

GOD: I suppose I am to blame. I made the life-desire so insistent that from this comes determined individualism and from this arises an egoism which causes each to think that he alone is fit to rule the cosmos. The great advance is for one to know he knows nothing and is not fit to rule anybody.

INGERSOLL: Let him be the cosmos for himself, and govern it for himself, but let him permit every other peaceable fellow also to be his own cosmos and his own governor.

GOD: But that would be wisdom. Wisdom comes slowly. Tolerance requires the intelligence to see that no one can ever be sure of anything and that none can be truly free till all are free.

MARGARET FULLER: Voltaire was saying that the tyranny of a cruel tyrant is often less destructive than the tyranny of a "good" man.

INGERSOLL: True. The tyranny of Nero or Caligula is less destructive to soul freedom than the tyranny of Puritans, Christians, and preachers, of Wayne Wheeler and the Y. M. C. A.

RABELAIS (*Aside*): *Qu'est-ce que c'est, mon ami,* Y. M. C. A.?

VOLTAIRE (*Aside*): I believe it is a religious order of perfect people.

RABELAIS: Perfect people. *Ciel.* How dull. *Et Vani Viller?*

INGERSOLL: O, Wayne Wheeler. He is the great American Drunkard. Kept at Washington as a horrible example.

RABELAIS:  *Comment?*

INGERSOLL:  Horrible example of a man drunk on his own egotism—only he is right. He is god.

GOD:  Patience. There have been many. Yet here I am. What were you saying of tyranny?

VOLTAIRE:  I was saying that great political tyrants are only interested in attacks on their power. The personal habits of their subjects are their own, but the religious fanatic—the "good" man—suppresses your habit of living, of enjoying life. By his immense egotism his morals must be your morals, his likes your likes, his dislikes your dislikes, his tastes your tastes.

GOD:  Which is all against my law of freedom for each individual to grow as an individual. Only that way can there be growth.

INGERSOLL:  The power to levy taxes and keep armies is what interests Caligula or any other ruler, but the power to regulate your very life and soul is demanded by the "good" man. He is determined to purify me to his brand of purity if he has to do it by fire. Caligula invades my pocket. The "good" man invades my soul.

RABELAIS:  Only the soul itself by its own inner desire can save the soul.

GOD:  And that is the whole truth of the matter, François. Jails never saved anything.

CARRIE NATION:  Drunkenness and obscenity ought not to be permitted.

GOD:  I permit them that the soul may be free.

JESUS:  Of what profit is it if you control by force; rather than that, the soul should be its own salvation.

CARRIE NATION:  Didn't you whip——

JESUS: No, no! Let us be done with that whip—that foolish story. Look at my life. Did I ever reply with violence?

GOD: I created life and all that is in life, and I gave man freedom to choose between good and evil. Whoever robs him of that freedom denies me.

(*A child seraph comes in.*)

CARRIE NATION: You permitted the war.

GOD: I tell you I permit life and everything that is in life. Good and bad—your salvation is to learn to choose good from evil. What war?

INGERSOLL: The great war on earth, the war to end war, the war for liberty, for democracy, the war to free the lesser peoples, the war for justice, the war to save civilization, the war——

MARK TWAIN: Hush, Bob, hush. You make me sick where my stomach was. I can smell those lies that baited the hooks of death for the young men.

MARGARET FULLER: Lies told to the mothers by "servants of the people," "sworn to serve the people."

MARK TWAIN: And they knew they were lies, and now brag about it as an old whore never does of her shame. Why, a fellow named Reel or Peel or Steel or Creel, and a general named Chowder or Crowder now actually brag that they worked up the young men to hatred and to death by a pack of lies these men knew were lies. So in France, so in England; each side is now telling of the lies with which it begot hate and lured the young men to death.

MORGAN: You can't do business without lies, and war is business—big business.

MARGARET FULLER: O, Lord, how could you permit it?

GOD: My law is freedom. I permit man to go to his destruction or his salvation according to his folly or his wisdom. Let him learn to know lies or die.

MARK TWAIN: In plain, earthly language, these young men who died in the fool war were fools.

INGERSOLL: No, Sam, were fooled, but the material was fine, the intention good.

MARK TWAIN: The Clam Chowder and the Fish Creel said it was necessary to manufacture lies in order to develop fear, hate, and a war psychology.

INGERSOLL: And these sworn to serve the people— and give them the truth.

MARK TWAIN: That shows who make wars, who carry on wars. The people? Pah—their bosses. The people—Dung.

CHILD SERAPH: What is war?

GOD: Man's supreme stupidity in greed. Whoever wins loses.

CHILD SERAPH: What does it do?

GOD: It destroys—always.

CHILD SERAPH: Destruction of what?

GOD: Property, body, soul.

CHILD SERAPH: But what does it accomplish?

GOD: Nothing.

CHILD SERAPH: Doesn't anything come out of it?

GOD: Yes; more wars.

CHILD SERAPH: You are making fun of me. Someone must like wars.

GOD: The rulers, the munition-makers, the international investors, but they are stupid. Their greed makes imperialism. Imperialism makes war. Wars eventually bankrupt and weaken the people and so the nations go to death. It is a long road but sure.

CHILD SERAPH: But why do they fight?

GOD: They fight on each side for gain, loot, colonies, markets, possessions—always gain—always greed.

CHILD SERAPH: Then someone does make a profit out of war?

GOD: Not in the long run. Sooner or later the fighting nation dies. Where is Egypt—Greece—Rome? England sees her death unless she can stop this fighting.

CHILD SERAPH: It all seems stupid. Why don't they stop?

GOD: No one has the courage to take the lead. No one is brave to stop by just stopping. No one trusts anyone.

CHILD SERAPH: Must it always go on?

GOD: Till man achieves wisdom.

CHILD SERAPH: When?

GOD: You visit earth, Jesus' earth. Attend a meeting of the American Legion—Daughters of the Revolution and Confederacy—call on General Fries of the Poison Gas Department, visit the movies, look at the herd; come back and tell me when man will achieve wisdom.

CHILD SERAPH: Do the people—those bankers, investors, traders—who make the wars, fight?

GOD: Long ago. A short, curly-headed fellow by the name of Alexander the Macedonian used to be first over the top; and an Englishman called "Lion-heart" was always in the thick of it. But that passed long ago. Really, it was stupid for the masters to fight when they could so easily make the people fight for them as well as work for them.

CHILD SERAPH: How?

GOD: Feeding them dope that made them crazy—"patriotism," "nationalism," "loyalty," "the flag" and other witchcraft words that made them hate and fear the rest of the world and believe they were the only good people on earth.

CHILD SERAPH: What do such words mean?

GOD: Nothing; nothing at all. Just medicine to make the people think that their country belongs to them; that it is the greatest country on earth; that their homes belong to them; that they are free men; that other peoples hate them and will attack them. Just lies. If no people believed these lies, peoples would not fight each other and there could be no wars.

CHILD SERAPH: The peoples must be very stupid.

GOD: Very. Samuel, from your earth experience, tell this child how wars are made.

MARK TWAIN: As unknown to the people as a burglary to the police. Diplomats—otherwise weasel men—just common men, awfully common, sitting safe in a room, listen to bankers, investors, merchant princes, also sitting safe in their chairs, shouting for their money bags, and generals and admirals also out of danger, shouting for their jobs; and the diplomats or "statesmen"—God help us—say something, write something, pull some wires, order out armies and navies, and war bursts before the people know it. They are then lied to to make them willing to die and pay the fiddler. It is so cheap and plain a game that it couldn't be played if the peoples of the different countries were not dumb cattle. The war is cooked by a few old men for the benefit of the moneyed rulers. Someone shouts the old hocus-pocus words—nation—loyalty, etc.—which really mean nothing but savage conceit and ignorance—and the people are just dippy to die and to load themselves with debt.

Christ's preachers in each land turn loose a bedlam of prayers to God to give their particular people power to make the most widows and orphans—to kill the most sons and fathers, and destroy the most cities in the name of Christ. Amen.

CHILD SERAPH: It is funny. Come take me over to Canopus—I want to play.

GOD: No. Float away by yourself for a time—I am busy.

CHILD SERAPH: Then I'll go to earth and see those funny little bugs that like to work and die for their masters.

(*Child Seraph goes out.*)

MARGARET FULLER: All war is hell.

MARK TWAIN: God's truth.

GOD: It is indeed, Samuel. War belonged to a period of tooth and claw—before reason had dawned. It is now the supremest folly of unintellectual man. What was the last great earth war about? What human good has it accomplished?

INGERSOLL: O, that holy war.

MARK TWAIN: Funny how all wars are holy.

INGERSOLL: On both sides—every side.

MARGARET FULLER: Alas, poor France! Always burdened with war debt—always at war.

VOLTAIRE: Yes. Millions for armies, navy, and imperialism; not a sou to pay her debts.

MARGARET FULLER: Alas, poor France!

VOLTAIRE: Spare us your pity, madame. At least we are not hypocrites. Since Charlemagne, France has been the Mars of Europe. *Par exemple*, witness modern France. Louis XIV took Alsace and Lorraine from Germany and rested his mailed feet on Italy as his footstool. Napoleon I was Mars incarnate. Alexander and Caesar were his ideals. He also conquered a world—only to have the tide ebb back to where it had been. The slaughter and the debt—for nothing. "The Little Corporal" was short—so in envy he shortened the Frenchman's stature an inch by killing off the best, and they stupidly died shouting "Glory." He made more widows and orphans than both his idols combined—that is his glory. His nephew—that superior barber Napoleon III —provoked the Franco-Prussian War in which Germany took back Alsace and Lorraine and now France has recovered them. Next!

MARGARET FULLER: But this Great War—the last?

VOLTAIRE: O no, madame. Not the last. By no means the last. But even there, France is not the helpless bee in the honey. We had a secret treaty with imperial Russia to attack Germany whenever Russia could provoke a war with her. Simple, madame. War on two fronts simultaneously for Germany. Austria opened the way and it was done. It is the prepared-for that always happens.

MARGARET FULLER: You astonish me. Were you not a Frenchman?

VOLTAIRE: No, madame. A Swiss watchmaker, and my time-pieces were good—excellent, I assure you. Shall I set you the hour for the next war?

MARGARET FULLER: O no. And what for?

VOLTAIRE: Always what for? Spoils, madame, spoils, spoils. Believe me, madame, France is the most martial nation in Europe. Even now though she will not pay her war debts she spares nothing for imperialism and military conquest. The lilies of France are red, madame.

MARGARET FULLER: And you, a Frenchman, say this?

VOLTAIRE: Yes, madame. I am not color blind. I love my fine, good, simple people of France, who are played with and murdered as much by the politicians of the Republic as by the diplomats of the Grand Monarchy. All peoples are good peoples, madame. Wars are never made by the peoples, but by the spiders who sit in the dark and spin webs to catch foolish flies. Buzz-buzz—the foolish young flies are caught in the web spread for them. It is too late. The war is on. It was for saying this that the masters of France drove me into the watch business in Switzerland. I hold my watch in my hand and wait for the next war.

RABELAIS: *Voilà. C'est vrai.*

GOD: Come, come, this is our picnic. Enjoy yourselves.

VOLTAIRE: Let the earth go to the devil.

MARK TWAIN: It will.

INGERSOLL: With war——

RABELAIS: *Le bon Seigneur* has spoken. Let us be happy.

MARGARET FULLER: Happy! And another war brewing—Women do not make wars.

CARRIE NATION: Who does make them?

GOD: I have just been telling a little seraph that wars are made by presidents, cabinets, rulers, armies, navies, diplomats, munition-makers and international investors.

INGERSOLL: The people—never.

MARK TWAIN: The people—Dung.

GOD: This is a picnic. Enjoy yourselves. Soon we must return to heaven. Robert, take Carrie for a walk.

INGERSOLL: Enjoy myself!

(*All go out laughing.*)

# XXIV
## God's Picnic and the Playwright

*(The Heavenly Meadow—starred with asphodels.* Jesus *comes in with a mutilated soul.)*

Jesus: Father, I found this poor soul lying senseless near the old gate. He has evidently fallen among thieves.

God: Perhaps he met some Christians.

Soul: Yes, sir. Some Christians and the police reformed me.

God: Their usual way. I have not seen such a wreck since that one from the Great War for freedom, democracy, etc.—what was he, that wreck?

Jesus: A pacifist, Father. He believed in me.

God: Yes. Not since that pacifist have I seen anyone so reformed, unformed, misformed, deformed as this. What was the trouble?

Soul: I wrote a play.

God: Well, by myself. I've written several.

Soul: May I sit down?

God: Certainly. You may do as you like. You may be wicked if you choose. This is heaven.

Carrie Nation: Wicked?

God: His wicked may be better than your good.

Carrie Nation: Jesus said: "Lead us not into evil, but deliver us from temptation."

JESUS: But not that we be walled about, knowing no temptation; rather that, meeting temptation, we be safely delivered.

GOD: Temptations are the soil from which grows character. They are as winds and tempests to the oak.

CARRIE NATION: Sometimes the tree falls.

GOD: Let it fall; I did not mean to save everything; I did not mean to save the weak, but man in his folly makes that his supreme effort.

JESUS: I did not ask that any be compelled by club and jail to be saved. Never.

GOD: Pity you have no followers, my son. Perhaps this is a true follower of yours.

MARK TWAIN: He looks it.

GOD: What did you say you did that brought you to this condition?

SOUL: I wrote a play.

GOD: Was it as bad as all this?

SOUL: No, Omniscience. It was a most excellent play, believe me, an excellent play. It was taken from life.

VOLTAIRE: Ah! A mistake.

SOUL: It was about a prostitute.

GOD: A what?

SOUL: A prostitute.

GOD: A politician?

SOUL: No, Omniscience; a prostitute.

MARK TWAIN: Perhaps he means a "journalist."

SOUL: No. My play was about a fallen woman.

GOD: How did she fall?

SOUL: That's it, Lord. That's just what I tried to show.

JESUS: Father, he means a woman who sells her body to a man.

GOD:   But some of your own best people do that.

CARRIE NATION:   In marriage.

GOD:   What's the difference?

JESUS:   No difference, Father.

CARRIE NATION:   Excuse me. Marriage is respectable.

JESUS:   I was never respectable.

GOD:   Well, well. I may be omniscient, but I cannot follow this nonsense.   So you wrote a play about
a Mary Magdalen?

SOUL:   Yes. And I showed that she was the natural
fruit of our social system.

GOD:   Where?

SOUL:   Earth, New York.

GOD:   She was, wasn't she?

SOUL:   Yes, Lord.   I showed the truth.

VOLTAIRE:   Another mistake.

GOD:   Well?

SOUL:   It was all true to life and ended in tragedy.

INGERSOLL:   Told the truth and it hurt.   Sure it
was a bad play.

SOUL:   The censor said it was a bad play and would
not allow it to be produced.

GOD:   Who said this?

SOUL:   The censor.

GOD:   Who is he?

SOUL:   He is just a common man.

VOLTAIRE:   Very common. He hates life, truth.

SOUL:   He says whether a play may or may not be
produced.

GOD:   Why, I wouldn't think of doing that myself.

SOUL:   He does. He decides if a play is good or bad
in a moral sense, not in a dramatic sense.

GOD:  I don't care what sense it is in.  It is nonsense. Who did you say dares do this?

SOUL:  The censor.

RABELAIS (*Aside*):  What are they saying?

VOLTAIRE (*Aside*):  They talk of one who decides when a play is good or bad.

RABELAIS (*Aside*):  Ah, a critic.

VOLTAIRE (*Aside*):  No.  The critic gives an opinion, advises; but the censor just forbids.

RABELAIS (*Aside*):  Ha! I know him, from Edgar l'Allen de Peau.  "Incensed by an unseen censor."

VOLTAIRE:  Yes.  Incensed by an unseen censor.

RABELAIS:  Yes, and the censor is swinging angels. *N'est-ce pas?*

SOUL:  Exactly.  The district attorney and a few long-eared fanatics are swinging angels.

INGERSOLL:  Back of the censor always a mob of mutts.  Their eyebrows are in the roots of their hair.

RABELAIS:  Ha! Chimpanzees.

INGERSOLL:  O no! Chimpanzees have some natural intelligence.

GOD:  But why your dishevelled appearance?  You certainly are not in my image.

SOUL:  Because, Omniscience, only my soul is here and this is my soul as the censor left it.

VOLTAIRE:  Everything I wrote was condemned. Life is always condemned  Truth is always condemned by the little beagles in office, who bark lest they be forgotten.  From the censor of morals, good Lord deliver us.

GOD:  Deliver yourselves.

MARK TWAIN:  The censor is a strangler approved by law.

INGERSOLL:   God save us from what the law approves.

GOD: Save yourselves.   If I should return you to earth——

SOUL:   No, no, Lord, not that!   I could write nothing now.   They have killed my soul.

GOD:   But if I sent you back, surely you could write about something.

SOUL:   O, candy pulls or church festivals—things where there is none of the mystery of life and of sex.

GOD:   Sex seems an awful thing to these people. Don't they know it is life itself?   How do they expect to know life?

SOUL:   O, they don't.   They don't want to.

GOD:   And won't.

SOUL:   One sex would have simplified the drama.

GOD:   I tried it.   It was not interesting.   Can you not discuss women on your stage?

SOUL:   Yes.   And make it real dirty too, if you will just insinuate or smear it with marriage.   You must not speak devoutly and plainly, as life does.   The censor, to do him justice, really doesn't object to smut and filth, nor do the good people—all they want is to have it in dirty allusions that make it disgustingly vulgar. To these they will crowd in hordes and laugh.

GOD:   They have a right to.   If hogs love swill let them have it.

SOUL:   But there are a few that hate swill and want life held up to them as in a mirror.

GOD:   They have a right to that.   Go on.

SOUL:   You must have no swear words.   The stage must be a Sunday-school picnic, or a vulgarly suggestive leg show.

CARRIE NATION:   They ought not to be permitted.

GOD: They ought to be permitted; everything should be permitted—for those who like it. Let like seek like. You will then know what you are.

CARRIE NATION: Well, I wouldn't permit them.

GOD: No, we know that.

CARRIE NATION: No one ought to be allowed to swear in public. I am with the censor.

VOLTAIRE: Unhappy man.

SOUL: O, since short skirts came in, leg shows have lost all suggestiveness and are beautiful, and you can swear all you like if you swear by strange gods.

GOD: What's that? What's that?

SOUL: I say, on the stage you may swear all you like if you swear by strange gods—by Jove, by Zeus, by Jupiter, by Heck.

GOD: Who is he? Heck? Never heard of him.

SOUL: He is a rural deity of New England, U. S. A., earth. You can swear by all the foreign gods, but not by you, Omnipotence.

GOD: What? Not by me? By myself, not by me?

SOUL: No, you can say "damn." It usually brings a laugh, but not "God damn" or "by God." You see God means you and he won't allow it.

GOD: Who won't allow it?

SOUL: The censor. You and Jesus cannot be produced on any stage.

GOD: What? Say that again——

SOUL: You and Jesus cannot be produced on the stage.

GOD: By myself, my son and I barred from the stage and I cannot be sworn by. Who dares this?

SOUL: The censor won't allow it.

GOD: He won't, won't he? By myself, I'll show that louse of a censor what it is when I take a hand in this meddling game. Allows in drama everybody but me and my son; allows oaths by all the old played-out alien gods and discriminates against me—the genuine, reliable, faithful, old naturalized Jehovah. Me—Me. Why, who has been winning all your wars for you, I'd like to know? Who's been attending to your weather for you and the crops and sending you prosperity?

VOLTAIRE (*Aside*): And earthquakes and epidemics.

GOD: I'll teach that censor to keep the home fires burning or I'll start one for him.

JESUS: Hell is abolished, Father.

GOD: O, I'll make one for his special benefit.

SOUL: The censor—No, not the censor—the church people back of him think you are too holy to be on the stage or to be spoken of out of church.

GOD: By myself, the stage is life and am I not life? I don't care what such fools think. Sappho's old god, and Virgil's old god, and all the dead and dying gods of the earth to be shown and sworn by, and I, the real, original, living and only Jew god, who made your dirty little pill in six days, I am to be stuffed onto the petty stage of a dark, stuffy church to be whined over and suffocated with incense. I can't come on the stage and nobody can swear by me. I'll be damned——

CARRIE NATION: O Lord!

VOLTAIRE: You can't be.

GOD: I can't, can't I? Of course I can. I can do anything. I say I'll be damned if I——

CARRIE NATION: No one can damn you, Lord; no one but yourself.

GOD: Keep quiet. No one but himself can damn anybody. That's the whole point. I certainly will not submit to this discrimination. I am going to be on earth and on every stage of earth. Big as life. I am life and Jesus is the life.

CARRIE NATION: You said yourself your name must not be taken in vain.

GOD: *Vain.* I'll be the judge of what is vain. I can take care of myself without the censor's help or yours. Do you suppose I need more protection than Jupiter, Zeus, Krishna, or Heck?

CARRIE NATION: But Jesus said swear not at all.

GOD: Keep quiet. You people know about as much as monkeys do about what Jesus said or meant. I don't intend to have oaths made by Zeus, Jove, and Heck and me left out. O by myself, I did think I could come off on a little quiet picnic and enjoy myself. That pill of an earth is always making trouble. I'll destroy it.

JESUS: O don't, Father. You promised you would not, not for a million years.

GOD: O but that censor, and that flock of putrid puritans. A million years of them!

JESUS: They'll be gone in less time than that.

GOD: They certainly will. By myself, I'll see to that.

SOUL: May I stay?

GOD: Certainly. Yes, stay. Write all the plays you want, about anything you like, present every shade of life, whatever comes to your imagination. Show man as he really is or as you conceive him to be. I'll produce your plays myself.

SOUL: O this is heaven.

# XXV

## RABELAIS AND CENSORS

(GOD's *picnic.* GOD *is lying under the tree of life,
his face covered with a cloud.* RABELAIS, MARK TWAIN,
VOLTAIRE, INGERSOLL, CARRIE NATION, MARGARET
FULLER, *and others in a group.*)

INGERSOLL:   That infernal censor about spoiled this
picnic.

MARK TWAIN:   Censors spoil anything.

VOLTAIRE:   How honest and refreshing Satan seems
in comparison.

RABELAIS:   Ah, Satan is an artist.

VOLTAIRE:   He deals with life as it is.

MARGARET FULLER:   It is the only interesting thing.

MARK TWAIN:   Rabelais, you were fortunate to have
lived before the putrid days of puritanism.   Today your
book would be prohibited by the censor.

VOLTAIRE:   Loathsome word.

MARK TWAIN:   Which—prohibited or censor?

VOLTAIRE:   Both.   Blights—mildews.

RABELAIS:   What is the matter with my book?

CARRIE NATION:   It is obscene.

RABELAIS:   Skip it.

CARRIE NATION:   I will not.

VOLTAIRE:   Of course not.

RABELAIS:   If it be obscene to you, then it is not for you.

CARRIE NATION:   It will corrupt the young.

RABELAIS:   Not unless they read it.

CARRIE NATION:   But they will read it.

RABELAIS:   Not unless they wish to.

CARRIE NATION:   But they will read out of curiosity.

VOLTAIRE:   Good.

RABELAIS:   The more you prohibit, the more curious they will be.   To prohibit is to arouse thirst.   My book has been on every bookstall for three hundred years and has never corrupted anybody.   If they like it, they are already corrupted.   If they do not like it, they are not corrupted.   Did you ever know anyone who was corrupted by it—or by a drama?

MARK TWAIN:   My friend, it is one of the great books of the world, but it would have been destroyed by a modern censor.   Yet you and Villon made the French language.   I have found deep wisdom, keen satire, and rollicking humor in your immortal book.

MARGARET FULLER:   So have I.   Much is not of our day but I skipped what offended me.   I never felt that because strawberries grow out of manure I must eat the manure also.

RABELAIS:   Ha! That is the very pulp of the melon. Some like garlic.   Some do not.   Yet our great good friend reposing there made the strawberries and the garlic.   Behold! He has spread for us a most sumptuous and abundant feast on a royal table.   There is a place for everyone, viands for every taste.   At this end are the most excellent great roasts of fat beef; haunches and saddles of mutton; capons with chestnuts; geese with truffles; tender, young ducklings, fattened on milk

curds, with the little new peas—beads of emerald and
jade; hams of the brave, curve-tusked wild boar; and
crispy, crackling, juicy roast suckling pig with apples
of Normandy. *Hélas!* Excuse me. I am overcome with
memories. And here on this table of bounty are pink-
suetted noble venisons and hares, pigeons, snipes, par-
tridges, and such-like slayers of starvation, and many
gifts from the great mother, the rolling, tumbling sea—
lobsters, oysters, mussels, bass, cod, turbots, and the like.
Here, too, are the ruby wines of Bordeaux and Burgundy, and the topaz wines of the Rhine and the
Moselle, and the rich strong wines of Xeres and Oporto,
and amphoral flagons and pot-bellied bottles of good
tonic liqueurs distilled by cowled and corded monks,
remote from the world—the sly ones—mixing prayers
and incantations with the many fine, fragrant medicinal
herbs. Forgive me, All-understanding One. I fear I
disturb you, but I feel the ghost of an earthly thirst
tickling my spiritual gullet.

GOD:  Go on, François, with your parable. I like it.

RABELAIS:  Ha! Well, here in the equator of this
great noble, royal table are huge pasties, hot and cold;
smoked bacon boiled with young cabbage shoots, or
nettle sprouts, or spinach, or whatever of the wilderness
of greens the lord of the feast has provided; and steam-
ing, vast bowls of tripes *en mode de Caen;* calves' heads,
pigs' feet; lambs' and beef tongues; liver-puddings;
dumplings; chitterlings; the sweet ink-fish; smelts;
sprats, shrimps, and all the tons of fine food the sea
pours forth to her nurslings, not forgetting her prolific,
fluent arms, the lakes and the rivers—pickerel, trout,
and sturgeon, Ha! and caviare and what other knick-
knacks, kickshaws, and thirst-producers, a good stomach may imagine. Scattered about as *hors d'oeuvres* are

olives, pickled and smoked herring, roasted wheat and nuts, radishes, green onions, salted anchovies, smoked salmon, pickled and spiced peaches and plums, and peppers, pâté of Strasbourg, and the whole great, good burgher family of sausages——

VOLTAIRE (*Aside*): There it is at last. I knew he couldn't forget his sausages.

RABELAIS: Little summer sausages of Switzerland, and the portentous, great sausages of Bologna—silver-gilt like a chamberlain's baton. *Eheu!* And kegs, casks, tuns of beer and ale—the light and the dark, the foamy new, full of the froth and violence of youth; and the quiet meditative old, with spice of the raw hops, as age is spiced with wisdom.

VOLTAIRE: Sometimes.

RABELAIS: These for the throats of those in coarse clothes whose hands are hard with pushing the world around. And at the other end—flagons of rich milk, cream and curds, softer than a maiden's bosom. *Eheu!* and that wonderful great family of cheese—the thick, the thin, the round, the square, the hard, the soft. Who shall name them—pebbles of bounty scattered by *Monseigneur* there, carelessly as he does the stars. Every region, country, and village has its own cheese of its particular quality—the Pont Evêque, the Port du Salut, Brie, Camembert, Bel-Paese, Parmesan, Limburger, Neufchatel, Rocquefort, Edam, Stilton, and Cheddar from the English who burned *La Pucelle*.

GOD: The English, François?

RABELAIS: Nevertheless they are most excellent cheeses, toasted with ale. *Eheu!* And the great, enormous, huge cheeses from the Pyrenees, large as a barrel; and from the Alps, large as a cartwheel. And here are the fine, thick, crusty loaves, and casks of Normandy cider, and a fountain of pure water, clear jellies and sweetmeats, and dainties. These for the fine, quiet women, and the children—the boys and girls who will some day sit at the head of the table. And what I have told you is only by way of example, hint, and suggestion. It does not scratch or pin-prick the offerings at this great table. I have not even mentioned the infinite variety of luscious and wonderful fruits— apples, peaches, pears, plums, figs, grapes. Ah, the grapes, beneficent clusters. And the tribe of berries and all the strange fruits of the hot tropics—bananas, pineapples, guavas, mangoes; oranges and lemons, golden apples of Hesperides. No one could tell the inexhaustible variety of this table though he had eternity to speak in.

VOLTAIRE: Do not encourage him, Lord.

RABELAIS: Here it is loaded and fully spread. No one need stand in one place, but may roam up and down—always there is elbow-room, for if some crowd as hogs, let them lustily be thrust aside. Surely at such a table is food to all tastes, and surely each will drift to that which he likes the best. And if some prefer swill and garbage, let them to it. Throw down the bars; let them guzzle, nuzzle, squeal, crowd, snort, swallow, both feet in the trough, to their fill till they lie down in the mire. There is no education of taste like freedom, and no cure like surfeit. Am I censored? No, vile as I am, I am free to all, yet whom have I corrupted? No, no, *mes amis*. Man corrupts himself and all impurity is in the eyes and ears of him who looks and hears.

INGERSOLL: Good, good. Very good, doctor.

MARK TWAIN: As a humorist who tried to be wise, let me bow to the wisest humorist of us all.

VOLTAIRE:   Ah, comrade, compatriot, I am at your feet.

GOD:   You have spoken for me, François.   All who speak for freedom, speak for me.   If some will have poison, let them to it.   It works its own cure.   I never lifted a finger to save anyone.   Let them save themselves.

RABELAIS:   Shall a censor say what my mind and soul shall eat and drink or in what be clothed?   As well tell my body what to eat and drink or what to wear.   No one can do that.

MARK TWAIN:   O, my friend and master, you left the earth too early.   That is exactly what they are now doing.   Backed by a policeman's billy, all manner of religious riff-raff, grafters, and soul-savers grow fat on telling you what you shall drink and not drink, and wherewithal you shall be clothed or not clothed, and with what you shall rejoice your mind.

CARRIE NATION:   Certainly.   Someone must stop this drinking, and someone must tell girls how to dress, and someone must tell the people what is indecent.

VOLTAIRE:   It would seem they should know for themselves.

CARRIE NATION:   Law should regulate women's dress for swimming.   Law should preserve modesty and morals by force if the people can't do it themselves.

RABELAIS:   Swimming would seem a time to dispense with clothes.

MARK TWAIN:   Exactly.   You would think that the very time you have the least need for a wardrobe. But anything can be made vile by a puritan—even swimming.   In the South Sea Islands no one wears any clothes.   All bathe in the sea together, men, women, and children, thoughtless as babes.

INGERSOLL: It is so in Japan, China, India.

CARRIE NATION: These are heathen.

INGERSOLL: Yes, before the missionaries got there to teach them impurity.

CARRIE NATION: At the bathing beaches women, by law, must wear stockings. That is right.

MARGARET FULLER: Are women's legs more delicate than men's?

MARK TWAIN: No. More indelicate.

MARGARET FULLER: And do they wear long gloves on the arms?

CARRIE NATION: No, arms are different.

MARGARET FULLER: I thought legs as well as arms were members of the same body.

GOD: I made both, and was perfectly innocent about it, but I see now since Peter's church got busy on the vileness of the body and the female sex, that I should have arranged for a one-piece suit of overalls for babies to be born in, two styles—boys and girls.

MARK TWAIN: The Sandwich Islands were a garden of Eden in the time of their innocence, before the missionaries came; nothing to do but pull your morning rolls from the bread-fruit tree and drink your cocoanut milk, brought by a trained monkey; no newspapers, no railways, subways, tramways, moral ways or other ways, no autos, no horns, no whistles, no smells, no noise, no Fourth of July, no politicians, no lies; neighbors bathing together at one reef, naked and not ashamed. If a man tried to run things, a banquet was arranged in his honor, and he was eaten. Sometimes a pig was also served, the heads of the pig and the guest of honor were exchanged so you couldn't tell which was which. I've noticed that, myself, at some banquets. In this way Captain Cook and some missionaries who tried to censor the first inhabitants were guests,—or should I say dishes?—of honor, and no after-dinner speeches. But yesterday I heard on my radio that a fellow named Desha has had an act passed by the legislature of Hawaii forbidding women to come into the beach streets of Honolulu in bathing dress.

INGERSOLL:  Bet Desha is a Christian.

MARK TWAIN:  You win.

INGERSOLL:  Bet he is a Reverend.

MARK TWAIN:  You win.

INGERSOLL:  Bet he is a missionary.

MARK TWAIN:  You win.

INGERSOLL:  Sure, I win.  To the impure all things are impure.

MARK TWAIN:  In the good old days they would have had a barbecue with Reverend Desha as the *pièce de résistance,* and the whole thing would have been settled pleasantly, with no heart-burnings that couldn't be cured by pepsin.

SAPPHO:  But why are legs more impure than arms?

MARK TWAIN:  I don't know.

VOLTAIRE:  I don't know.

INGERSOLL:  I don't know.

GOD:  I don't know.

SAPPHO:  Reverend Father, why are legs impure?

RABELAIS:  Daughter, are they impure to you?  Are they impure to a child?  Except ye become as one of these ye cannot enter into the kingdom of God.

JESUS:  Except ye be pure as little children are, ye defile the world.

GOD:  Children, let me explain.  Diseased minds of ascetics have been teaching for centuries that sex is impure, therefore the body is impure.  These narrow fanatics have belied me by making impurity a part of religion. They have taught that legs and the mother breasts of women are impure and must be covered.

INGERSOLL: And the impuritans of every class and creed have spread this.

GOD: This rottenness comes from repressed sex desires. All monks, nuns, priests, preachers, clergymen, and such like are people of repressed sex desires and are rottenly erotic. For them the legs are not a graceful part of a beautiful body used for walking, running, dancing, and the like, but are only pillars to the temple of Priapus, and this filthy rot is taught to children from their infancy, as a part of religion, so the sewer current flows on. My son, do you not see that it is always your people who insult me.

JESUS: O not my people. But forgive them, Father, they know not what they do. Let us try them for the million years.

GOD: Dear, gentle, beloved optimist. This has been a disturbed picnic. Let us now return to the bustle and din of heaven. O those earth-souls and their harps! I dread them.

# XXVI

## CENSORSHIP

(GOD *is resting on an easy throne in the Cerulean Portico. A* CHILD SERAPH *comes in.*)

CHILD SERAPH: Father—Father.

GOD: Eh—what? What's the matter?

CHILD SERAPH: Gimme a ride.

GOD: A ride? You seem to think I've nothing in the universe to do but give you rides.

CHILD SERAPH: Gimme a ride.

GOD: Get on my toe.

(CHILD SERAPH *mounts* GOD'S *foot and* GOD *gives her a ride.*)

CHILD SERAPH: Father, what is a censor?

GOD: O, for my sake—where did you get that infernal word?

CHILD SERAPH: I heard Peter tell Gabriel you said he was a censor. He seemed worried.

GOD: He ought to be. Get off now.

(CHILD SERAPH *dismounts*).
What else did he say?

CHILD SERAPH: Said he was only looking after people's morals.

GOD: Exactly. That's what they all say. Nobody seems to understand that in my sight everyone's morals are each one's own affair.

CHILD SERAPH:   What are morals?

(VOLTAIRE, RABELAIS, MARGARET FULLER, MARY WOLLSTONECRAFT, ROBERT INGERSOLL, MARK TWAIN, CARRIE NATION, *and* BEN FRANKLIN *come in.*)

GOD (*to the Newcomers*): Welcome! (*to the* CHILD SERAPH): What did you say?

CHILD SERAPH:   What are morals?

GOD:   Customs, that's all.   It is moral in China and Turkey to have several wives—but very immoral in the United States of America—earth—to have more than one.

MARK TWAIN:   Openly.

GOD:   Yes, yes.   Anything is moral anywhere if it is concealed.

MARY WOLLSTONECRAFT:   But isn't concealment contemptible?

GOD:   Of course—cowardly, contemptible—shabby. Don't think I am approving.   Myself forbid—I am only trying to give this pure young angel an idea of earthly morals.   I don't think she'll get it.

CHILD SERAPH:   Yes, I will, if they are pure and true.

GOD:   Ah, but they are not.

CHILD SERAPH:   Well, go on.

GOD:   At one time it is very immoral for a woman to show her ankles.   At another time in the same country it is perfectly moral to show her knees.   In the United States it is moral for her to show her beautiful legs on the street but immoral to show her beautiful back and bosom bare.   It is moral to bare her back and bosom at a dinner party but not moral to bare her legs at a dinner party.   It is moral to be nearly naked on a beach but not in a parlor.   Sometimes there is a clash in morals.   Very good people—Methodists, Baptists,

Catholics—think it is immoral for women to show bare legs, bosoms, backs at all—women are supposed to be terrapin, drawing neck and legs and arms under cover.

CHILD SERAPH: I certainly don't understand. I think you are making fun of me.

GOD: O, no—not of you. It used to be immoral for women to smoke—now it is moral. Morals are chiefly concerned with sex. The very best morals is not to know the difference between a man and a woman or how babies are created—or if you do know, you must never allude to it. Keep it dark. Let no one find out. Now do you understand?

CHILD SERAPH: No, I think it is stupid and very vulgar.

GOD: So do I.

CHILD SERAPH: What is a censor?

GOD: I thought you had forgotten that. I don't seem to be very good at explaining man's funny ideas. (*To the group*.) You tell her.

MARK TWAIN: A censor is a fool. Men are to live as he wills.

INGERSOLL: An egotistical tyrant.

MARK TWAIN: All wisdom will die with him.

INGERSOLL: A conceited bigot executing the will of conceited bigots.

BEN FRANKLIN: A meddler in other people's business.

MARGARET FULLER: A strangler of thought. You cannot legislate morality. Have they legislated monogamy or temperance?

MARK TWAIN: A censor is a skunk squirting stench on what was clean.

MARY WOLLSTONECRAFT: A slave-driver, whipping the backs of art, drama, poetry, literature, destroying their life.

MARK TWAIN:   He and his kind are the ones who drive little boys to the Bible and the dictionary to find obscene words.   Instead of making the wonder of sex open and pure to adolescence they make it dark, smutty and criminal, and privies are chosen libraries for the obscene explosions of dawning manhood.

CARRIE NATION:   You can't let people do and say just what they like.

GOD:   O, but I do.

CARRIE NATION:   People should have liberty but not license.

MARK TWAIN:   God, that silly lying phrase makes me sick.

GOD:   Yes, Samuel.   Freedom is my universal law and license is only another word for freedom.   There can be no qualification of freedom or it is not freedom.

INGERSOLL:   That fool phrase was invented by those defenders of the past—fossil judges—to enable them to deny freedom rather than to deny property-privilege.

MARK TWAIN:   Mossbacks in black silk nighties.

CARRIE NATION:   But think what would become of society if all were free to say and write and do as they pleased.

VOLTAIRE:   *Ma fois,* it would be wonderful!

INGERSOLL:   Yes.   Development in freedom.

BEN FRANKLIN:   The world is sick for it.

CARRIE NATION:   I suppose you would not restrain burglary.

MARGARET FULLER:   O, Carrie.   You disgrace woman's intellect.

MARK TWAIN:   O carry me back to ole Virginny.

Like all slaves, women believe in the whip and club.

MARGARET FULLER:   Not all women.

INGERSOLL:   They haven't been free long enough.

VOLTAIRE:   Who is free?

CARRIE NATION:   Well, would you restrain a burglar?

BEN FRANKLIN:   A grain of sense is worth a ton of argument.   If Carrie were a man I would say she is a simpleton and drop the subject, but as she belongs to a newly enfranchised and highly emotional group, I will suggest that the difference between burglary and free conduct is that burglary and such crimes are invasions and usually by force.   It is always permitted to resist force with force (unless you are a Christian, which is another matter for other argument).   It is always permitted to resist invasion. But if I only speak, where is the force?   If you voluntarily read my book or see my play, where is the invasion?   You have freely done what you chose to do.   Others may think you have bad taste, but that is your affair, not theirs.

RABELAIS:   *De gustibus non est disputandum.*   O wise Romans.

BEN FRANKLIN:   Exactly.   There can be no argument about people's taste.   Each is a law unto himself.

VOLTAIRE:   *Chacun à son goût.*

BEN FRANKLIN: Yes, each must decide as to his own likes and dislikes.   If those having power may suppress books and plays they do not like, then those having power may suppress prayer meetings and patriotic speeches they do not like.

INGERSOLL:   Exactly.   Catholics may suppress Protestants and Protestants Catholics, a Chinese theatre be raided for showing a rape scene and an American theatre be raided by Chinese for showing the murder of a father by a son.    It all resolves itself into the opinions of the ruling power.

MARGARET FULLER:    Always wrong—reactionary.

MARK TWAIN:    Worse.  It becomes the mere opinion of the censor.

INGERSOLL:    Worse.  Of the chief of police.

BEN FRANKLIN:    What tyranny!  What suppression of thought!

VOLTAIRE:    Mildew of art.

MARGARET FULLER:    Frost upon social growth.

GOD:    This censorship is a denial of my first law—freedom—unqualified, absolute freedom.  Only in that atmosphere can man live and grow.  Suppose the caveman had established a censorship?  Where would the world be today?  All growth is the breaking down of censorships.

VOLTAIRE:    What infinite harm, obstruction, delay, and sowing of tares and thistles was done by medieval censorship.

INGERSOLL:    Weeds that have lasted until now. From this old religious censorship comes the abominable obscene sex puritanism, sex consciousness of today.

MARK TWAIN:    Making a cesspool of the earth. Nature from manure brings flowers and fruits.    It might be by the same wonderful alchemy she would make from obscenity something vital and fine.

GOD:    She would.  It is my law.  But there must be the sunlight of freedom.  Whatever a person seeks voluntarily can do no harm.  He will either swallow it or spew it out.  It is either for him or not for him, and by my law he must be let alone to make his choice. He will choose what his real nature contemplates.

MARK TWAIN:    Did anyone ever meet a person who

would confess that so-called obscene literature or plays had injured him?

GOD: Never. Each finds or fails to find what he is looking for. He remains the same.

RABELAIS: The obscenity is in him, not in the book.

GOD: But to hold freedom by the hand requires great courage. Freedom is not for the stupid or the weak.

VOLTAIRE: Alas, for man!

MARGARET FULLER: Alas, for man!

MARK TWAIN: Man gets what he deserves. When the United States—earth—Jesus' earth—our earth— intended to dispossess Spotted-Tail's band of Sioux Indians of their lands in favor of squatters, a commission was sent, as usual, to perform the robbery under the guise of a new treaty. The commission was composed of decayed politicians—lame ducks——

RABELAIS (*Aside*): *Qu'est-ce que c'est?*

VOLTAIRE (*Aside*): *Je ne sais pas.*

MARK TWAIN: A council was called to meet on the reservation. At the appointed time the long council tepee was set up and the seats for the messengers from the "Great Father," the President . . .

INGERSOLL: Good God! Were they ever in Washington?

MARK TWAIN: Seats for the messengers of the Great Father and buffalo-robe couches for the chiefs, sub-chiefs, and headmen of the tribe were arranged around the sides of the council lodge. Some buffalo rawhides painted with pictures of the hunting and war prowess of the Sioux were in the walls of the tepee to inspire the warriors.

The Indians began to come in slowly, day by day,

till by the day appointed for the council there were many hundreds camped in the willows by the creek, but no squaws, or only a few as camp tenders—no children.

To those acquainted with Indians this looked bad. In case of trouble they would be ready for the warpath unencumbered, and when one has war in mind and is ready for it, it is easy to make it.

MARGARET FULLER:   Same as now.

VOLTAIRE:   Always the same.

MARK TWAIN:   It was very picturesque to see the young men in ceremonial dress: eagle-feather bonnets, painted faces, painted horses; manes and tails braided with eagle feathers and a show of perfect horsemanship, as brandishing rifles and bows they galloped in circles; wheeling, turning, kicking up a whirlwind of dust: a golden cloud in the sunlight through which shone the naked red bodies, the white, black, red, and piebald horses, the headdresses, quivers, whips, leggings, and all the paraphernalia of many colors.   On the council day the commission came in long coats and faces; the interpreters, reporters, attendants, and the curious from the ranches and the frontier town, wearing slouch hats, flannel shirts, and overalls.

The commission went into the council tepee with the Indian Agent and interpreters and then followed the chiefs and headmen.   Last of all came Spotted Tail himself, head chief of the whole Sioux nation: tall, grave, lean, wrapped in a blanket, his scalplock tied with a strap of otter fur, his hair hanging in two braids on his chest, his face, as if hewn out with a hatchet, his eyes looking neither to right nor left, yet seeing all. So with great dignity he entered the council.

Outside the tepee were the few whites, curiosity-seekers, and the hundreds of Indians, mostly young men, crowding close to the tepee to catch what might be said within. Thus the council began. The head commissioner through an interpreter told how the Great Father always had in mind the welfare of his red children—our brothers.

INGERSOLL: Same old hypocrisy.

MARGARET FULLER: The world-old lie of imperialism.

MARK TWAIN: Yes, you know the bunk. Well, it ended with the fact that for the good of their health and happiness there was to be a new treaty and they were to be moved to another reservation.

Spotted Tail replied in low, deep, guttural tones, beautifully modulated as a chant, rising and falling as is the manner of the Indian language. He said that this reservation had been given to them many years before by solemn treaty with their fathers and the Great Father; the bones of their fathers lay buried in this soil; the place had become to them as the shell to the river-mussel—they were content and did not wish to move.

So the sparring went on, back and forth; the commission growing more emphatic, showing the claws. Suddenly a young man, but one of the headmen, sprang to his feet and said loudly that this had gone on long enough. It was plain the white men intended, once more, to break their solemn word and drive the Indians from their home. As for him, he was as willing to die now as later. It must surely come to a fight, so let it begin now. A surge of Ah's (yes) ran through the tepee—especially from the younger men.

The listening crowd outside were fired—Ah—Ah—Ah—(Yes—yes—yes) like the muttering of a coming

storm.   They crowded more eagerly closer to the tepee.
The orator felt the approval and his strength.   He
spoke louder—he became impassioned.

"Let us look to our mother, not to the Great Father
—our mother who bore us, the earth, who bore us and
will take us back as she has taken back our fathers.

"Our fathers will fight with us.   Let us begin now
by taking the scalps of these who have come to rob us.
I will lead you."   The young men leaped to their feet.
Weapons are not allowed in council, but there were
plenty outside where the crowd was shouting assent and
giving the shrill war-whoop.   Massacre was not two
minutes away when Spotted Tail leaped forward and
faced the orator.   "Stop.   Who are you that now speaks
in council for the Sioux Nation?   Are you a chief?
No, I know who you are—you are a puppy at the
campfire.   Your name is Sitting Bull.   What have you
done?   Nothing.   Do you know what I have done?
Before you were born I led the Sioux in battle against
the Crows, and drove them to the mountains.   But the
whites are like the grass in spring, on the prairie; you
cannot overcome them.   The end is sure.   Yet I am
ready to die.   I am old.   It is easy for me to die, but
if I were young I would be ready to give my life for
my people.   It may be that I, an old man, will choose
to lay my bones with those of our fathers.   But now
this boy is asking the Sioux Nation to break the sacred
council law.   He has sat in council yet stirs up the
people to break the council faith.   He wants us to kill
the men whom we have asked to come here to meet us
and who sit now in the sacred council lodge.   Hear me,
chiefs and men of the Sioux tribe. These white men shall
go safe.   They shall take back what answer the chiefs
have to give.   Until then they are my brothers, and if

any one"—a long pause—"lays a hand on them"—a pause—"I will kill him.

"Do you know who I am who say this? I am Spotted Tail, Chief of the Sioux Nation. I am no squaw. I am a *man*—and if you don't believe it, look at this." He dropped his blanket from his shoulders and lifted into view that which is looked for by every mother and those around her to know whether a man child has been born. A moron would have laughed at this phallic gesture, a puritan would have sought a censor—and the police. But the men saved from massacre knew that in a life and death drama it was a solemn testimony of manhood and an appeal to God.

GOD: Right, Samuel, right. It was the testimony of the life which I have created.

MARK TWAIN: God, damn the censor.

GOD: No—Samuel—no. Man must damn his own follies. Let him never ask me for help against his own stupidity.

MARGARET FULLER: What is the remedy?

GOD: Freedom, but it takes courage.

MARGARET FULLER: And when?

GOD: When man has courage to pay the price. Always for every good there is a price.

CHILD SERAPH: Give me a ride.

GOD: Let us all ride through the starry ways.

(*All go out.*)

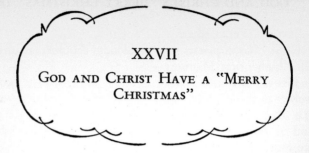

## XXVII

## GOD AND CHRIST HAVE A "MERRY CHRISTMAS"

(GOD *and* JESUS *are sitting by the family fireside.*)

JESUS:   Father, I wish you'd come down to earth with me.

GOD:   What for?

JESUS:   You know they always celebrate my birthday on the earth.

GOD:   Yes.   They're very particular about that one day.   They give presents and the poor a dinner.   You don't expect me to——

JESUS:   No, Father—I know—they have commercialized Christmas; but there is the war.

GOD: O that doesn't amount to much.   It will be forgotten in thirty years and they will have another. We agreed that the common people never have any quarrel with each other.

JESUS:   Yes, Father.

GOD:   And I showed you that not all your teaching will bring peace while this competition of a greedy few for exploitation at home and abroad goes on.

JESUS:   Yes, I know we agreed to that, but——

GOD:   I told you, didn't I, that the self-interest of all must insist on peace instead of the blind self-interest of a few finding advantage in war?

JESUS: Yes, Father.

GOD: Your priests are as bloody shouters as any. This high priest Manning——

JESUS: I know, Father. There have always been wolves in sheep's clothing, but what I was going to say was that the troubles on earth are war and poverty, and as poverty is the mother of suffering, I thought we might help men to end it.

GOD: End what?

JESUS: Poverty.

GOD: When you end poverty you will end war. The root is the same. The rich and the poor are forever at war at home. The rich work the poor, then the rich war between themselves as nations and send the poor out to be killed, and they take the survivors back to work. There are always plenty of poor.

JESUS: Let us go to their help and tell them these truths. Poverty and war have the same root. Let us help the people to tear them up.

GOD: You haven't forgotten what men did to you?

JESUS: I know.

GOD: You know what they do to all their saviors?

JESUS: Yes. Death.

GOD: I was going to take a rest and now you want me to go down and save a nest of hornets whose brains are in their tails.

JESUS: I can't help feeling sorry for them. Their very stupidity is to me pitiful.

GOD: They give the poor a dinner on your birthday.

JESUS: O Father, let us show men that the world will be happier, including the rich few themselves, if these will do justice and think only of the welfare of all.

GOD: Do you think they will do it?

JESUS: Let us try. Surely they do not want millions to suffer that they may be burdened with more than enough.

GOD: Very well, beloved optimist. I will go with you.

JESUS: How shall we appear to them?

GOD: We might descend in a fiery cloud and work miracles or appear just as men preaching on the streets.

JESUS: Do you think they will know us?

GOD: If man cannot see the God in a soap-box orator, he cannot find God anywhere. Where's your mother?

JESUS: She is welcoming some Jewish martyrs, who have just been killed by Russian Christians.

GOD: Tell her we are going to earth, but we won't be gone long.

JESUS: But, Father, it may take us a very long time to make men see the truth.

GOD: Nevertheless, tell your mother we won't be gone long.

(JESUS *goes out.*)

My dearly beloved son. He knows love is the God in man—He knows love is the only constructive force —but he does not know the stupidity of his poor animals and that they are liable to be exterminated before they learn.

(GOD *goes out.*)

(GOD *and* JESUS *have returned from earth to their heavenly mansion. They join a group who are earnestly watching them.* INGERSOLL, MARK TWAIN, MARGARET FULLER, *and others.*)

GOD: Well, my son, we weren't long, were we? I

am glad to get back, but I must say I had the time of my life. Hand me my slippers, Job. Wasn't that judge funny who sentenced us, taking himself so seriously, all ballooned up in a black silk wrapper, pursing his thin lips, rolling his words on his tongue as if he were in love with his own voice; talking of "rights of property," "law and order," "safety of society." Amusing ass. What was his name? That was funny too.

JESUS: Kenesaw Mountain Landis.

GOD: What a name! What a fool!

INGERSOLL: He isn't a judge. He's a baseball player.

GOD: What, not another Sunday person?

INGERSOLL: Well—similar. Mountain's hysteria is patriotism—and Billy's puritanism. Why this Kickshaw person sent a lot of young men to jail for twenty years—for having some I. W. W. cards in their pockets. Twenty years—twenty young years, and they had not done a thing or said a word; just the cards in their pockets.

GOD: That's nothing. He sentenced me to be hung.

JESUS: Yes, both of us. We were soap-boxing, the police started a riot as an excuse to kill us or jail us, and commenced firing; one policeman was killed by somebody, nobody knows by whom, and we were arrested and hung. All we said was that society was still in the feudal ages having the few so very rich, owning everything, and the millions so very poor, and the lowest millions, having nothing, dangerously degenerating the race.

GOD: Yes, and you ventured to say that war was

un-Christian.   You remember he said we had attacked the very foundations of society and betrayed the republic and incited murder—but he was glad to see that I at least could feel remorse.

JESUS:   Yes, I remember that.

GOD:   I was laughing so hard at the solemn fool and his stale kingly talk about loyalty and patriotism.   I had to hide my head.   Well, well, it's good to be home again.   I told you we wouldn't be gone long.

JESUS:   I don't understand it.   When I was killed before, they let me preach for nearly ten years before they killed me.

GOD:   Efficiency, my son, efficiency.   Everyone worships property more than flesh and blood.   Your own priests are supporters of the privileged property class.   It owns the church, the school, the press, the bench, the legislature.

JESUS:   But, Father, do you think it does any good to resist evil by force?

GOD:   By myself!   Does it do any good to let evil trample the life out of you?   Life is all resistance to evil.   Your friends down there slay microbes, mad dogs, malarial mosquitoes, and other things which threaten their lives, then why not slay the poison microbes of society?

JESUS:   But what you call the diseases of society are evil laws, customs, institutions.   You cannot slay institutions.

GOD:   Slay them by education.   I said thou shalt do no murder.   Murdering persons does no good.   It is the rulers who always provoke the killing.   They killed you to save their institutions, didn't they?

JESUS:   Yes.

GOD: Exactly. If the riders will not get off the people's backs but kill those who try to throw them off, the people in their turn kill also—the masters provoke bloodshed. Revolutions are only a part of evolution, and all evolution is through the death of the old that the new may live. Remember, it is always the few who refuse to get off the backs of the many who provoke the bloodshed. Always those on top choke freedom of speech and begin the killing. Rulers force the bloody revolutions—always.

JESUS: To take life is wicked and debasing.

GOD: Society is taking life every day. You and I were hung because we threatened the existence of their special-privilege institutions. But suppose, on the other hand, there had been enough of us to kill them and save ourselves. What then?

JESUS: Still the killing is not right. It advances nothing.

GOD: No. It is stupid—but so long as the masters begin with jails and scaffolds for those who speak against the institutions of privilege, revolutions will be bloody.

JESUS: Yes, but to get enough people to act together, is impossible until you convince their minds, and certainly you cannot convince their minds by force.

GOD: No. Even defensive force can only go so far as reason has prepared the way. Force is always stupid, but the masters compel it.

JESUS: But you and I had not said a word about using force. We hadn't advocated killing anybody. They killed us because a policeman who was clubbing us was killed by somebody.

GOD: Exactly. The policeman began it. The master class of one nation will not stand any interference from without by another nation, and the master class within a nation will not stand any interference from within by anyone. It is all one. The real reason they hung us was because we were attacking their privileges and trying to arouse the people to thought.

JESUS: Yes, I know they hung us because of their fear.

GOD: It was like a frightened boy trampling a mouse. Really they are breeding a bloody revolution. Stupidity, stupidity—always stupidity—masters and slaves, both stupid.

JESUS: But, of course, they didn't know any better.

GOD: Of course, they didn't know any better. Just stupid. I thought I'd die laughing at your expression when those three detectives swore you had for a long time threatened to kill their comrade who was shot— you, the Prince of Peace, who had only been on earth a day.

JESUS: That perjury and hatred filled me with sadness.

GOD: That's because you persist in claiming a sort of kinship with these creatures.

JESUS: But, Father, what am I to do to bring about the brotherhood of man, the universal peace?

GOD: Nothing.

JESUS: Nothing?

GOD: Nothing: but continue to preach the force of love and the wisdom of the Golden Rule.

JESUS: Must I keep on being killed every once in awhile because I cry out for justice for the poor?

GOD: Yes, my son. Always you will be killed by men devoted to law and order. Why, nothing was more law-and-order-like than your crucifixion. Where is Peter?

JESUS: He is out in south heaven. Father, I must say I haven't had a very happy birthday.

GOD: My dear son, truly I am sorry. No one who thinks can have a Merry Christmas. You were born to be crucified.

# XXVIII
## Denver Prays for Rain

(GOD *holds a new star in his hand; turning it slowly, carefully, examining it. Around him are angels and archangels.* GABRIEL *and* HERMES *in attendance.*)

GOD: Hermes, what is that awful buzzing in the radio?

HERMES: God Almighty, I will see.

GOD: Gabriel, have one of the electricians look into it—Volta, Steinmetz, Franklin—somebody.

GABRIEL: Yes, Lord.

HERMES: I can't make head or tail of it; just a lot of groaning and buzzing.

GOD: Gabriel, see if you can understand it.

HERMES: It reminds me of a pair of bellows Hephaestus once had at his forge—whines, groans, sighs, sobs, squeaks, and nothing but wind.

GABRIEL: I know. It's a prayer.

HERMES: That's what I said. Nothing but wind.

GOD: A prayer? From the earth, of course?

GABRIEL: From the earth.

GOD: Of course. Is this the earth sabbath?

GABRIEL: No, Lord.

GOD: Then why on earth are they praying?

GABRIEL: They are in trouble.

GOD: O yes—they do also pray when they are in trouble. What's the matter?

GABRIEL: They want rain.

GOD: Who wants rain?

GABRIEL: Denver, Colorado, United States, Earth.

GOD: Why do they bother me for every little local, petty, particular want? Don't they understand that I have a whole universe on my hands? They mean nothing to me——•

GABRIEL: No. They only think of themselves.

GOD: Well, I have to admit that is one of my laws. Where is Aquarius?

HERMES: I don't know. Out on his job, I guess.

GOD: Call him—quickly.

(HERMES *goes out.* ST. PETER *comes in.*)

Peter, you are the very person I want to see. Who started this habit of praying to me for picnic weather, crop weather, haying weather—for babies, automobiles, new pants—and successful jelly? Do your people think I have nothing to do but run a department store for their benefit?

ST. PETER: Why, people always prayed and offered up sacrifice, didn't they?

GOD: Yes. For really big things—to win a war or something like that—but these little foolish local troubles—Denver wants rain.

ST. PETER: Jesus told us to ask.

GOD: But there is reason in all things. He didn't mean you to ask for jam on your bread or more coal in the cellar or more wine.

ST. PETER: More wine? Excuse me, Omniscience. No one today would think of praying for wine.

GOD: Why not? If for water?

ST. PETER: It would be wicked.

GOD:   What would be wicked?

ST. PETER:   To pray for wine. Besides it would be simpler to see a bootlegger.

GOD:   A bootlegger? Ah, yes. I remember. Someone said Jesus was one at Cana.  Well, Peter, if your church is responsible for this prayer habit, stop it. Ah, there is Aquarius.

(AQUARIUS *comes in with his watering pot.*)

AQUARIUS:   Here I am, Lord.

GOD:   Where were you?

AQUARIUS:   Watering the Atlantic Ocean.

GOD:   Is that necessary?

AQUARIUS:   No, but I felt like it.

GOD:   Why don't you water—what's the place?

GABRIEL:   Denver, Colorado, United States, Earth.

GOD:   Yes, that. Why not water that? They are howling—I mean, praying—for rain, and you watering the Atlantic.

AQUARIUS:   The Atlantic is on my circuit. You told me to water when I felt like it.  When I get over the Atlantic I feel like watering. I think it's the water that does it—so much water.

GOD:   Well, for my sake, hurry over to Denver, Colorado, United States, Earth, and feel like watering there. Give them plenty.

AQUARIUS:   My pot's nearly empty.

GOD:   I will fill it. Go on—hurry. Give Denver plenty of water.  Water it so I never hear from it again.

AQUARIUS:   I'll do my best but this pot is pretty old and ——

GOD:   O hurry up! You are always grumbling.

(AQUARIUS *goes out.*)

GOD:   Did you ever see such a literal, stupid, ob-

AQUARIUS ANSWERS A PRAYER

stinate old fellow in your life?  And I have to trust
watering the earth to him.  Peter, give your attention,
your personal attention, to your church.  If it is responsible for praying every time somebody wants rain
or sun or something, stop it.

St. Peter:  I don't think it is my church.  We are
well organized and don't bother you much. It's those
other fellows—Methodists.  They are ignorant people;
Baptists.  Ha!  It's the Baptists—they are strong on
water.  It would be just like them to water their
prayers.

God:  O, by myself, there goes that radio again.
Gabriel, see what it is; that simply cannot be a prayer.

Gabriel:  Yes, it is, Lord.  It's a prayer.

God:  A prayer? That a prayer?

Gabriel:  Yes, Omniscience.  A prayer.

God:  Sounds more like a riot. Well, what is it now?

Gabriel:  It's from Denver, Colorado, United
States, Earth.

God:  O for my sake. Tell Aquarius to hurry up.

Gabriel:  Yes, Lord—wait—Lord, wait—no—
they say it is pouring torrents.  They want you to stop
it.

God:  Want me to stop it?  By myself, do they
think I have nothing to do but dance attendance on
them?

Gabriel:  They say it is another deluge.

God:  Where's Noah?  Where is Noah?  Somebody
find Noah.

Gabriel:  The rivers have flooded, dams burst,
houses washed away, fields covered with mud, crops
ruined, and still it pours in sheets.

God:  Confound that stupid Aquarius.  He has no

discretion.    Hermes, tell Aquarius to stop.    Hurry, Hermes, hurry.    I certainly will have to find another water-carrrier with more discretion.

HERMES:    Instantly, Lord.

GOD:    First they pray for rain, then they pray to stop the rain.    Impudence.    Do they think I have nothing to do but watch Denver, Colorado, U. S. A., Earth?

GABRIEL:    Now a fight is going on.    Two Reverends, when the rain began, each laid claim to having produced it by prayer; now the people want to lynch them.

GOD:    What's that?

GABRIEL:    I don't know, Omniscience.    I think it is Christian.

GOD:    Whatever it is I hope they do it.    Go on.

GABRIEL:    And each now declares the flood is the other's fault.    One pounds his pulpit——

GOD:    What's that?

GABRIEL:    I don't know.    I just give it as the radio gives it.

GOD:    Yes.    Well?

GABRIEL:    One pounds his pulpit and shouts: "Enough, Lord, enough."    And the other bangs his fist on the Bible and shouts: "Lord, this is ridiculous." Boats are in the streets.

GOD:    Send Noah.    I tell you they need a sailor.

HERMES:    He has stopped.

GOD:    Who?    Noah?

HERMES:    No, Aquarius.

GOD:    Well, it's time.    Never mind about Noah.

HERMES:    Here comes Aquarius, Lord; he wants to see you.

GOD:    What does he want?

HERMES: He wants to talk to you about his job. He says he doesn't understand it.

GOD: I should say he didn't, but he'll have to keep it.

HERMES: He says he can't please everybody.

GOD: Neither can I. Now don't disturb me. I want to examine this star. There goes that infernal radio again. What is it now? More prayer?

GABRIEL: Not exactly. The Denver Power and Light Company want to thank you through the Reverend Jenkins Undershot for the recent abundant rains.

GOD: Huh! Glad somebody's pleased. Disconnect that radio.

(*All go out.*)

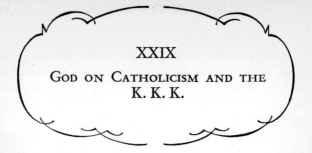

# XXIX

## God on Catholicism and the K. K. K.

(GOD *is on his throne at the Elysian Fields, and has just thrown an asteroid to* HERCULES *to open the games. Around the throne are* MARGARET FULLER, SAPPHO, CARRIE NATION, MARK TWAIN, ROBERT INGERSOLL, THOMAS PAINE, VOLTAIRE, *and* RABELAIS. GABRIEL *and* HERMES *nearby.*)

GOD: Is this one of the athletes approaching?

INGERSOLL: I think not, Omnipotence.

GOD: He looks it.

INGERSOLL: He certainly is a husky soul.

MARGARET FULLER: Not much soul.

GOD: Patience, Margaret; I begin low, but there is the germ of a soul in everyone. Where is Peter?

HERMES: I think, Omnipotence, he is over at the fly-casting competition.

GOD: Yes, that must interest him. It is a new sport to him. Poor old fisherman. Since I took away his gate he does not know what to do.

HERMES: He tries to be cheerful, Omnipotence, but he is quite sad.

GOD: He will find an occupation. Gabriel, bring me this bulky soul. Hermes, find Peter and tell him I would like to see him.

HERMES: Instantly, Omnipotence.

(GABRIEL *and* HERMES *go out*.)

THOMAS PAINE: Peter ought to be glad to be released. It is a great responsibility to say who shall be shut out of heaven.

VOLTAIRE: Or come in.

RABELAIS: *Hélas!*

GOD: O, his post carried authority. That was the trouble. Power over others is always a destruction to development and is always abused. I was pretty mean myself in my old Jehovah days. But I, too, have evolved. Well, well, welcome, my friend.

SOUL: God, I've had a dirty deal.

GOD: Then you were dealing dirt. What you give to others you receive again.

SOUL: No, Lord. I was all right, but the other side were scoundrels.

VOLTAIRE (*Aside*): He is too perfect.

RABELAIS (*Aside*): In his own conceit. O, intolerable perfection!

GOD: Who are you?

SOUL: In my earthly existence, I was——

GOD: That terrible earth!

SOUL: I was S. Glenn Young, Kleagle of the K.K.K.

GOD: What?

SOUL: Kleagle of the K.K.K.

GOD: Don't stutter so. The what? Speak slowly.

SOUL: Kleagle of the K.K.K.

GOD: By myself, I don't understand you.

MARK TWAIN: Kumpny of Kowards wearing Knighties. They spell Khrist with a K. An eagle is a kleagle and an idiot is a kidiot.

VOLTAIRE: The imbecile mind has its advantages.

GOD: But this K.K.K.—what is its meaning?

MARK TWAIN: Kontemptible Kidnaping Kowards.

SOUL: I'm not going to stand for this. Where is my nighty and my gun?

GOD: This is heaven, my son. Neither nightshirts nor guns.

SOUL: I don't care what it is. I won't stand for any abuse; if I can't shoot somebody, I have no business to be here.

VOLTAIRE (*Aside*): True.

SOUL: It was a D.D.

GOD: A what?

RABELAIS: A Doctor of Divinity?

SOUL: Hell, no. A "Dirty Deal."

GOD: Tell me about it.

(ST. PETER *comes in.*)

ST. PETER: Lord, did you send for me?

GOD: Yes, Peter—a moment. I hope I did not interrupt your sport?

ST. PETER: No, it is the most foolish fishing—all on dry land, with little bare hooks—foolish. They'll never catch anything. We never did that on Galilee.

GOD: Please wait while I hear this soul. Go on. Tell me.

SOUL: Well, I was leader of the Ku Klux Klan.

MARK TWAIN: He admits it.

SOUL: In Herrin——

ST. PETER: What did he say? A herring? Is he a brother fisherman?

SOUL: No, Herrin—a town in Illinois, on earth.

ST. PETER: Oh!

SOUL: And I was cleaning up the town for Christ. I had to shoot some and do a little killing and flogging, but the Methodists encouraged me.

GOD: Yes. So with Methodist approval you shot some people for Christ?

SOUL: Yes, to make them decent citizens.

VOLTAIRE: Doubtless it did.

GOD: And the D.D.?

SOUL: The Methodists?

GOD: No, the dirty deal.

SOUL: Why, I was shooting the lawbreakers, and some dirty scoundrel shot me and here I am.

MARK TWAIN: Good shot.

SOUL: I should say I was, and all I was doing was to make them keep the law.

GOD: I see. I see. Reform with a big R and a big gun.

SOUL: Exactly. You get me.

VOLTAIRE (*Aside*): An old idea.

INGERSOLL: Never old—prohibition.

ST. PETER: I know this K.K.K. I told you about them. Their creed is force, their rule of life, intolerance.

GOD: Never mind, Peter. Wait.

SOUL: Well, if there is a law against drinking, or having wine in your house, and people won't keep the law unless you shoot them, you've got to shoot them, haven't you?

GOD: Wine? Shoot them to stop the use of wine?

SOUL: Yes, wine and whiskey and beer; everything but lemonade and whistle.

GOD: Is not what they drink their own business? Jesus approved of wine.

SOUL: He never did. I tell you we know better— He used unfermented grape-juice.

RABELAIS: *Mon Dieu! Mon Dieu!*

GOD: Go on. You were shooting people, whipping them, and breaking down their doors and so forth for their good.

SOUL: Yes. To make them obey the law.

PAINE: You had to break all the law and the Constitution of your land to make others obey your fanaticism.

SOUL: All we asked of them was to be good the way we told them to be. Also we intend to drive out the Catholics.

ST. PETER: Ha!

RABELAIS: Ha!

GOD: Patience.

VOLTAIRE (*Aside*): God asks too much.

GOD: Go on. The Catholics—you intend to drive out the Catholics. Why?

SOUL: They are un-American.

PAINE: And you are American?

SOUL: One hundred per cent.

MARK TWAIN: O hell. "Do his bit" "one hundred per cent." They make me sick—hell.

GOD: It is abolished, Samuel. Go on.

SOUL: One hundred per cent. No liquor, no niggers, no Catholics, and the "Stars and Stripes" forever, flying over the Land of Liberty.

INGERSOLL: It makes me sick too.

GOD: Here, Robert. Take a little stimulant. Genuine nectar.

INGERSOLL: Thanks to God—Is Wayne Wheeler here?

GOD: No—and never will be. I have made a new rule—the stupid shall not enter heaven. Why are the Catholics un-American?

SOUL: They owe allegiance to the Pope, not to the United States.

INGERSOLL: Millions of Catholics have died for this country in peace as well as war.

SOUL:   They take the dictates of the priests.

INGERSOLL:   And you of the preachers.

SOUL:   They vote as the priests say.

INGERSOLL:   And you as the bosses say. Listen, my friend, the Catholic church has built up political power by the votes it controls.

SOUL:   Yes, yes, that's it.  It is un-American.

INGERSOLL:   What's un-American about it?  So have the Methodist and the Baptist church.  What is un-American in controlling votes for political power? It may be bad—and the people may be dummies—but it is not un-American.

SOUL:   But the Catholic church heads in Rome——

INGERSOLL:   So it does.  And the church claims political power and authority as well as spiritual power and authority.  It will be up to the American people to disapprove at the polls, not by guns and nighties. We have taken the dictates of foreign governments before now.

SOUL:   They control the schools, the courts, the political offices.

INGERSOLL:   Suppose they do.  What's un-American about it?  If they do it is by political influence.  They use the same lawful political methods that Methodists and Baptists use, but the Catholics are more clever at it. They have more solidarity.  They stick together better. It may be bad, but what's un-American about it?

SOUL:   Exactly.  They stick together better, that means they are Catholics before they are Americans— always Catholics first.  The mass of them are ignorant foreigners and take the political dictates of the priests.

INGERSOLL:   Educate them.  Educate them.  The law allows that.

SOUL:   Damn education.  The Catholics do their

own education. They catch 'em young. Separating spiritual authority from political authority is all bunk, you can't expect a person brought up to obey the priests spiritually not to obey them politically. Don't we ask every American to have no foreign allegiance? Well Catholics do have allegiance to a foreign political power.

INGERSOLL: Well, what do Catholics do contrary to law?

SOUL: Nothing, damn 'em. They are too smart. I believe you are a Catholic. What is your name?

INGERSOLL: Robert Ingersoll.

SOUL: My God!

GOD: Yes. What is it?

SOUL: Ingersoll, the atheist? In heaven?

GOD: Shake off your earthly fog. Reason—winged reason—is my most god-like gift to man. Do you think I am angry when man uses the gift I have given him? You would be the better for it. Go on.

ST. PETER: A moment, Omnipotence. May I ask this soul—it is a soul, is it not?

GOD: Well, ask your question.

ST. PETER: Has my church done anything forbidden by law or the United States Constitution, anything you can indict its members for?

SOUL: No, I tell you. They are too smart. That's the trouble.

MARK TWAIN: It hasn't tried to hide in masks and nightshirts.

INGERSOLL: It hasn't encouraged shooting up a town, raiding homes, and whipping women, has it?

ST. PETER: Jesus said: "Resist not evil," but you take guns and whips to what you conceive to be a political menace.

THOMAS PAINE:   This soul's Kumpny of Kowards think to support the law by breaking the law.

SOUL:   We are prohibitionists, and prohibition is above all law.   It is God's law.   Ask Wayne Wheeler.

GOD:   Stop, stop!   There never was a law of mine that had the word "prohibition" in it.   Neither the word nor the spirit.   I work by growth and education of the soul not legislation of the soul.

SOUL:   Excuse me.   Wayne Wheeler and the Reverend I. E. Lee of Herrin know better.   They say, and I say prohibition is God's will, and we were going to put it over if I had to kill every damn bootlegger in Williamson County.   We know what is best for the people.

PAINE:   Exactly.   *You* are prohibitionists, and what *you* think is gospel.   Why don't you take a hint from these same Catholics and learn that not force but education promotes a cause; that to compel obedience never has taught anything.   Suppose somebody stronger than you thinks drink is good for you and forces it on you.

SOUL:   I'd smash him too quick.   No one can tell me what I ought to do.   All the preachers approved what I did.

INGERSOLL:   Of course they did.   They have approved every fire that ever burned a witch, and every violence and villainy that ever whipped the human soul down to earth.

GOD:   Enough.   Enough.   Masks, nighties, guns, whips, brute force, intolerance.   I have heard enough. Hermes, take this soul to the African Medicine Man's heaven and deliver it to William Sabbath.

INGERSOLL:   Sunday, Omniscience.

GOD:   Ah, yes, Sunday.   I never can remember his

name.　Leave them to stew together in their intolerance and ignorance.　Now let us have a little innocent recreation.

SOUL:　Today is Sunday.

GOD:　You are going to him.　Learn that correction is by education and reason, not by force—Catholicism or Prohibition.　Act by discussion not by guns.

(HERMES *leads out the* SOUL.)

ALL:　Thank you, Lord.　What a relief.

GOD:　What's the cheering for?

HERMES:　Shelley on Pegasus has just won the "Poets Handicap" by a nose.

GOD:　Good.　The poets are always ahead.　Let us watch the game.

(*All go out.*)

A POETRY RACE IN HEAVEN

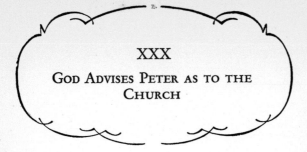

# XXX

## GOD ADVISES PETER AS TO THE CHURCH

(GOD *is in his private studio. Before him in a vase of purest crystal is a spray of apple blossoms. A bee is burrowing into one flower. A piece of honeycomb is in a crystal plate on the marble table. Present are* JESUS, BUDDHA, GAUTAMA, LAO-TZE, VOLTAIRE, RABELAIS, MARK TWAIN, SAPPHO, *and* MARY WOLLSTONECRAFT. HERMES *stands near.* GOD *touches one of the apple blossoms.*)

GOD: Is it not beautiful?

JESUS: The symbol of a pure soul.

BUDDHA: Naked beauty.

LAO-TZE: It shows the path. To bud, to blossom, to bear fruit. Each step a destiny fulfilled through freedom. Seed for the future, honey at the core; growth on growth, to the ultimate.

GOD: It is just as wonderful as a star.

BUDDHA: You must be glad you made it.

GOD: What? You too, Gautama? That childish superstition—I "made it." I made nothing. I did greater than that—I established eternal conditions out of which all things create themselves and grow: heavenly bodies, these beautiful blossoms and the fruit to be, and man.

205

MARK TWAIN: The fool. He spoils everything except the stars—them he cannot reach.

GOD: Consider this little bee. What airplane of your earth equals its ancient mechanism and power? Its fuel is only a drop of sugar. The stars are not more true to their courses than the nectar-gatherer to her especial doorstep. Consider, too, the engineering of this honeycomb; the social order of the hive, how wise!

MARY WOLLSTONECRAFT: They kill all males after using the chosen. How wise!

RABELAIS: Ha! *Les femmes sages et les sages femmes.*

MARK TWAIN: Clever little devils.

GOD: I do not advocate this. I advocate nothing. Evolution must be free. Women may yet find a real use for men. How much more beautiful a miracle it is that the infinity of life and matter, color and form come from immaculate, invariable, and fixed conditions rather than that I or anyone creates specially each form of the infinite.

MARK TWAIN: Lord, won't you work just one miracle? Give man a mind to understand what you have said.

GOD: I work no miracles. He must understand or pass away.

MARK TWAIN: And no great loss.

GOD: No. Nothing is a loss that passes by its own worthlessness.

VOLTAIRE: Man's egotism will destroy him.

INGERSOLL: Witness—Woodrow Wilson. He sought re-election on the slogan "He kept us out of war," well knowing he intended to join the pandemonium. He heartened the world with the rhetoric of the Fourteen Points and broke the heart of the world by abandoning them. He went into the war on freedom of the seas, and never mentioned freedom of the seas at the Peace Conference. He gave college valedictories on freedom and democracy, and understood neither. He was a combination of Presbyterian preacher and Southern slaveholder. Long after all other countries had released their political prisoners, he kept in consumption-breeding penitentiaries pacifists who had defied him—victims of his vanity, his pitiless egotism.

VOLTAIRE: Egotism, a mildew that destroys all.

INGERSOLL: How humble are the truly great; knowing that they know nothing. Take the scientists: they lust not after power, but guessing man's place in the wide cosmos and how he came to be, they are always lowly minded; never sure. The religious people are cocksure; these know all and know that in all time and space only they are right.

SOCRATES: Who thinks that he knows all knows nothing. The oracle once said of me that I was the wisest of men. That puzzled me, for I knew it was not true, and yet I did not like to think the god of the oracle had lied. So I began to study men, especially the priests and politicians. Whenever I heard of a man accounted wise I questioned him. Always I found that he thought he was wise. He was sure he was right, but in fact he knew nothing. I found I was the only man who knew that he knew nothing. In that way I was the wisest. Priests are the worst of all, for instead of searching nature's facts, from which to draw belief, they have a lot of ancient superstitions not founded on any fact, and when a fact of nature contradicts these sacred myths, they, in conceited ignorance, will not reject the myth, but, as they cannot change great nature and eternal cosmos, persecute and put to death the rare, brave ones who have a little seen the true god, the eternal cosmic one, who manifests himself in facts, not in superstitions. Superstitions are the remains of a past ignorance—these the churches adore.

INGERSOLL: God save us from the churches.

GOD: Save yourselves. Ha, that reminds me. Graceful Sky-Cleaver, will you be so kind as to tell Peter I would speak with him.

HERMES: A pleasure, Omnipotence.

(HERMES *goes out.*)

MARY WOLLSTONECRAFT: I often think of what Socrates has said—the terrible power of churches. They are the outgrowth of man's childish fears and ignorance, opposing thought or any change.

GOD: One of my conditions is there must be ceaseless change.

MARK TWAIN: Man is a dung-beetle; he looks behind him.

VOLTAIRE: Every church is the left arm of rulers.

MARK TWAIN: And what is the right, my fellow humorist?

VOLTAIRE: The armies—one chains the mind, the poor mass mind; the other binds the poor, great, stupid body.

RABELAIS: The church, the one, true, great Mother Church, holds heaven's gate and decides who shall pass through. That is a power stronger than armies.

VOLTAIRE: It fetters the mind, and is used as all power is—for the rulers—Church and State. Twins always.

GOD: There is no gate to heaven.

RABELAIS: Ah, but *Monseigneur,* that is something the people do not know, and will the church tell them? No. No. Does a man cut down his fruit tree? No.

INGERSOLL:  O, every church is a worldly institution, an institution carefully organized with little rituals, kneelings, risings, passwords and initiations; these
ceremonies cover up the fact that they are worldly
institutions of property, organs of worldly wealth and
worldly power.

MARK TWAIN:  They are joss-houses; pull down the
idols and let the people see how dead they are.

VOLTAIRE:  They are temples of ignorance. Teach
the child to think for himself and they will fall.

RABELAIS:  Ah, but they hold the keys to the doorway beyond the grave.  Ha! If I have the keys, even
to a wine cellar, I am a power.  The saintly, beatific,
and beatified wine cellar.

GOD:  No one holds keys to the doorway beyond
the grave.

RABELAIS:  Ha! But Omniscience, the people do
not know that.

MARK TWAIN:  The people—dung.

(HERMES comes in with ST. PETER.)

ST. PETER:  Lord, I am here.

GOD:  Peter, I want to talk to you very seriously
about your church.

ST. PETER:  What is the matter now, Omnipotence?

GOD:  I do not wonder you say "Now." It is now
exactly what it has always been.  Your church opposes
freedom of thought.  It sets up authority against individual thought; always it opposes anything new.  I
told you once before there has not been a great human
discovery or a great human thought your church has
not opposed with its worldly authority, its absolute
temporal power and un-Christian punishments. Bruno,
Savonarola, Galileo, Jeanne d'Arc are only samples of
its persecutions.  It has as bitterly opposed all modern

scientific discoveries of Darwin, Wallace, Huxley, Tyndall, Pasteur; every earnest servitor of man and thought and me; and as for childish tales of miracles and virgin births—well, you are simply intellectually hopeless.

RABELAIS: We only insist on one virgin birth, Omniscience. We have no wish to make it general. Though that, too, would have its advantages.

VOLTAIRE: It would.

GOD: If you can have one virgin birth, you can have millions. You know, or you should know, these puerile, primitive, impossible conceits insult my wisdom and deny my eternal conditions; which know no exceptions or any manner of altering.

ST. PETER: We have accepted, Lord, much scientific truth.

MARK TWAIN: After the world has accepted it.

ST. PETER: We have contributed scientists of our own.

GOD: What good is that? After the whole profane and heathen world have accepted? Why can't your church for once be at the front of human thought and take the lead?

VOLTAIRE (*Aside*): *Mon Dieu.* You ask too much.

GOD: —instead of sitting back in a medieval cell of the Dark Ages, throwing stones at every brave thinker if he happens to differ from the——

INGERSOLL: Omnipotence, the Jew Bible of three thousand years ago is surely more exact in scientific truth.

GOD: Robert, you are a humorist. And the dogmas of the church made a thousand years back in darkest ignorance are, I suppose, more true than modern science.

ST. PETER: You haven't joined the Ku Klux Klan, have you, Omnipotence?

GOD: What's that?

ST. PETER: It's a sect on earth that bitterly assails Catholics, and seeks to destroy your church.

GOD: Hush—*your* church. Not mine. No. Never heard of them. You know I hate all persecution; whether by Catholics or against them. How do they assail?

ST. PETER: With clubs, rifles, whips.

GOD: Then do not fear.

MARK TWAIN: And nighties.

GOD: You need fear nothing but education.

ST. PETER: My church is honest when it opposes free thought.

GOD: So is the Ku Klux Klan, I dare say. So much the worse. You had better be intelligent and tolerant. Honesty in evil-doing is no excuse. I dare say Bruno was roasted very honestly, and Galileo honestly imprisoned. That doesn't help them, or truth, or freedom, and does not excuse a church that pretends to act for my dear son and in his name.

ST. PETER: O, not pretend.

RABELAIS: *Le pauvre Pierre.* He is on one of his own fish-hooks.

GOD: Then prove 'tis not pretense by acting as Jesus taught. Did you ever burn people for differing with you, my son?

JESUS: Never.

GOD: Or for their opinions?

JESUS: Never.

GOD: Did you ever teach a worldly power to judge and punish human thought through all the ages?

JESUS: Never. Love and forgiveness, tolerance and charity were my whole dogma and absolute freedom—mind and body.

GOD: There. You hear the head, or supposed head, of your own church.

MARK TWAIN: I am almost sorry for this Simple Simon Peter.

INGERSOLL: God told us he was merciless. He is. Truth always is.

ST. PETER: Hear me, Omnipotence, and you, my Lord and Savior. When I was with you in the flesh, you were not a world-wide institution, holding great temporal power. There were not then great princes of the Church and a Pontiff, supreme as God, who sits with kings. But now the hope of this power is not to allow the people to think.

RABELAIS: *Vrai, vrai!* If the bottom bricks are pulled out the house crumbles.

MARY WOLLSTONECRAFT (*Aside*): Poor old Peter.

ST. PETER: Are you not proud of your great church?

JESUS: I am not. It is not my church. Shall I be proud of force, of authority, of discipline, of ignorance? My power is spiritual and my kingdom is not of this world.

ST. PETER: You are not proud of your own church?

JESUS: Peter, understand once for all, it is not my church. Of all men you should know 'tis not my church. When did I seek power, authority, or wealth? When did I build palaces while the poor starve, or where do you find my command for a worldly, temporal institution that by its authority controls the very thoughts and tongues of men? Cast in your net again, good Simon Peter.

St. Peter: Are there no good men in the church?
No good priests?

Jesus: Yea, Simon Peter. Many. A great mul-
titude—gentle and loving souls, giving their lives in
poverty, with self-sacrifice to the service of the Father,
as did you and the brethren. But this church, this institution that uses your name is not poor, this church
does not make self-sacrifice, this institution seeks political power. I speak not of priests as men, but of the
church, that institution, that machine, which with its
traditions, dogmas, ambitions, and gowned politicians,
grasps at worldly power; sucking the honey of these
beautiful lives and using it to its ambitious purposes.
Its thirst for political place and power will be the death
of the church. Men have a right to distrust a church
that is not single and humble for the spiritual life I
brought.

St. Peter: My Lord and Master, on earth I followed you in adoration for I believed love is the only
power and you are love. I thought these churchmen
through the centuries, these princes of the church,
wiser than I.

Jesus: What have I to do with princes? Were you
a prince of my church? I had no church. Is a stable
and a manger noble birth? Let a man so live that he
makes noble the straw where first he wailed. That is
the only nobility.

St. Peter: Once more I cast myself before you,
Lord.

Jesus: Rise, Peter, rise. Place your tired head upon
my bosom.

St. Peter: But Lord, you said to me: "Thou art
Peter, and upon this rock I will build my church, and
I will give unto thee the keys of the Kingdom of

Heaven, and whatsoever thou shalt bind on earth shall be bound in heaven, and whatsoever thou shalt loose on earth shall be loosed in heaven."

JESUS: O, simple Peter. And were you really a rock? And did I hand you any actual keys or cords? And did you think I meant to build a church with brick and stone? I, who said my church would not be built with hands? I, who sat with publicans and died upon the cross between two thieves? Did I not also say to *all* the brethren: "Whatsoever ye shall bind on earth shall be bound in heaven, and whatsoever you shall loose on earth shall be loosed in heaven"? I did not say "whomsoever" ye shall bind, or "whomsoever" ye shall loose. Why do you trifle with words? Did I not always speak in parables and symbols and with mystery? Shall it be that in my mouth, which said "judge not," shall be found a command to judge? Do you think I ever gave power to men to judge of their fellows or to say who shall enter into the Kingdom of Heaven? Shall any man usurp the very judgment seat of God?

MARY WOLLSTONECRAFT: Poor old Peter.

VOLTAIRE: He has cast his net and caught a huge, brass vessel, in which is imprisoned a powerful jinni.

MARK TWAIN: Fisherman's luck.

VOLTAIRE: An Old Man of the Sea.

ST. PETER: Lord, I never understood these labyrinths of the church, but I thought the great men of your church knew better than I.

JESUS: Ah, yes, you thought it was my church. Many have thought so. I have no church—none. I want none—save in each one's own soul. Whosoever seeks after power and authority is not of me.

ST. PETER: The church that came after me founded

itself upon these words: Whatsoever ye shall bind on earth shall be bound in heaven.

JESUS: A foundation of sand. In that same hour did I not also say "that if two of you shall agree on earth as touching anything that they shall ask, it shall be done for them of my Father, which is in heaven"?

ST. PETER: Yes, Lord. You said this.

JESUS: And has it been done?

ST. PETER: No, Lord.

RABELAIS: My luck, too. *Hélas!* How many good and very learned, eloquent, and pitiful prayers I have made in good, classical Latin, not trusting church Latin, and in Hebrew, that God might have no excuse for not understanding; and not one, never a one answered. I might as well have prayed to the gargoyle on the Cathedral of Notre-Dame. And yet there stood the promise. I got not only two to agree, but the whole fraternity —never a prayer granted.

VOLTAIRE: With me the same, but I was not a priest. You should be glad to listen to this exposition.

RABELAIS: It is a great opportunity.

JESUS: And have you not seen through all the centuries the pestilence rage, and wars and famines devour, and droughts and tempests and the lava-flows mercilessly continue in spite of the prayers of the church and the faithful?

ST. PETER: Yes, Lord. It is so.

JESUS: And because of this, am I a liar? Have my words deceived you, or do you deceive yourselves? Always I have spoken in a mystical spirit and in parables and symbols hoping for that transfiguration of man's soul which maketh all things possible.

ST. PETER: Yea, Lord. I believe.

JESUS: Not only you, Peter, but every one who believes in me as love and not as hate, forgiveness and not vengeance; tolerance and not intolerance is a rock on which I will build my church, but my church shall not be builded of hands, but shall be the soul of each one who believes, and whatsoever any such soul binds in love upon earth shall be that instant bound in the great heaven of love which encompasses the universe, and whatever such a one looses for love's sake shall be that instant loosened in the heaven that is within him.  And whatever two shall agree to ask, or one solitary and alone on the ocean waste or the mountain top, that shall be answered of himself to himself instantly, because he has asked.  But if he ask that the tides be stayed or the eternal mechanics of the universe be broken, he is the child of folly and he has not understood me.  He must ask of his own soul what his own soul has power to grant unto him.

St. Peter:  Lord, I understand.  I have seen the images of the saints and the holy crucifix itself burned by the lava-flow which relentlessly passed on to destroy the vines and the habitations.

Jesus:  Peter, nothing is holy but the life and living love.  Is it not better these dead emblems should be burned than that the everlasting should be overturned and lava turn in its flow and run up hill?

St. Peter:  But the cry which the images figure?

Jesus:  Is it not the greater mercy that the conditions be changeless through eternity?  Life is large, Peter.  Time is long.  The earth is a ball of clay.  Shall Aldebaran be shaken from his course because a man prays, or a church demands?  This is ignorance and folly.

St. Peter:  It is the greater glory and mercy of God that the conditions be fixed forever.

GOD: Yes, Peter. You see the truth at last. I suppose, like all else, the church that calls itself your church will have to work out its own salvation, or its own destruction, according to the fixed conditions. And yet, Peter, I sent for you to help you. I wanted to call your attention to the fact that Prince Bishop Bertram of Silesia and Eastern Germany has forbidden the marriage ceremony, or other rites of the church, to women who do not fully cover their bosoms, arms, and legs.

VOLTAIRE: What a mistake that woman has legs.

RABELAIS: Or a bosom.

MARY WOLLSTONECRAFT: Or arms.

INGERSOLL: She should have been a lump.

MARK TWAIN: Fit mate for man.

GOD: Cardinal La Fontaine and his bishops disapprove of all sports such as swimming, tennis, and the like, because these athletic sports, though good exercise, make a girl forget her legs. The cardinal and his bishops declare no woman shall be permitted at any religious ceremony whose neck and bosom are exposed, and the Pope, your successor, Peter, approves.

ST. PETER: Approves what?

GOD: O, not the neck and the legs, but covering up my sculpturing.

ST. PETER: Omnipotence, I can't help it. I am in the Pope's hands.

VOLTAIRE: Unhappy fisherman.

GOD: So I thought. So I thought. Therefore I was going to suggest to you that these "Eunuchs of God" who control your church have inherited from centuries of eunuchism a vile tradition that the body is vile, and a woman is vile, and sex is vile, and my greatest miracle, if you choose to call it so, my greatest miracle of all—

birth—is vile. The time has come, Peter, to tell you very clearly that these morbid thoughts so insulting to me and to my finest handiwork—woman—have their origin from diseased minds. These thoughts about wicked legs, bosoms, and arms come from the suppressed sex desires of these eunuchs of God.

RABELAIS: *Hélas!* Only of God. Otherwise—Ha!

VOLTAIRE: Purer minded if really eunuchs.

GOD: These eunuchs are themselves violating my greatest law. When they call themselves eunuchs of God, they take my name in vain. They are really not normal, wholesome persons, sound or clean as a child is clean, or as a young man is clean who only sees beauty and purity and my miracle in woman.

MARK TWAIN: Good. Go on, Lord.

GOD: Thank you, Samuel. They make of her an obscene instead of a divine thing.

VOLTAIRE: Bravo!

GOD: These proclamations and fulminations by the princes of the church, eunuchs of God, are doing more to debauch the minds of young women than anything else possibly could. They make filthy what I have made pure. They stimulate unnatural thoughts that would not arise in a pure, healthy girl's mind, nor in a man's either; in the obscene way these eunuchs insist on. They actually teach obscenity. No man created in my image——

VOLTAIRE (*Aside*): Unmutilated.

GOD: ——who unsexes himself for "the greater glory of God" is capable of understanding either my glory or the innate purity of woman. Yet girls and women look to them as holy men, teachers. They are really corrupters of youth.

St. Peter: What can I do, Lord? I have no influence in the church.

Voltaire (*Aside*): Poor fellow.

God: I see your difficulty. You can't put brains into people with a syringe.

Voltaire (*Aside*): Not even eunuchs.

God: But I do wish that the princes of your church could get it into their unsexed——

Voltaire (*Aside*): Or oversexed——

God: ——heads that the body I created in my image is pure, all pure, and is not laid out in tracts, regions, and parts of purity and parts of impurity.

Ingersoll (*Aside*): Like Chicago.

God: I was going to suggest to you that for once the church come out of the Middle Ages. It must go the way of free evolution or it will go to destruction. That Klux—what was that foolish name?

St. Peter: Ku Klux Klan.

God: Yes. That Ku Klux Klan will not destroy a spiritual church that seeks not worldly authority and political power. But so sure as it lusts after political power its rivals will combat that which is not the humble teacher of Christ's spirit but at heart is an Italian political hierarchy. When it enters that arena it must expect to be met as a political menace. Let us join the company.

(*All go out.*)

XXXI

BISHOP WILLIAM MONTGOMERY
BROWN ENTERS HEAVEN

## BISHOP WILLIAM MONTGOMERY BROWN
## ENTERS HEAVEN

(*A Heavenly Terrace.  A Group: the* VIRGIN MARY,
ST. PETER, INGERSOLL, MARK TWAIN, VOLTAIRE,
RABELAIS, *and others.  A* LONE SOUL *approaches.*)

ST. PETER:  Here comes another.  Nowadays they
come from anywhere, everywhere.  Walk right in.  It
is all so unexciting—so helpless.  Like fishing with
a bare hook.

INGERSOLL:  Who is this?

MARK TWAIN:  Hard to tell.  Heaven isn't as monotonous as it used to be when Peter guarded the wicket.

INGERSOLL:  More interesting.

MARK TWAIN:  Sure.  Real people.

VOLTAIRE:  The unorthodox.

RABELAIS:  There is more life, *esprit.*

MARK TWAIN:  Music is not the only thing now.
They are taking up other arts, and even science.  Music
is broadening—the Angelic Harp and Choral Society
offered me the position of conductor.

INGERSOLL:  You?

VOLTAIRE:  You?

MARK TWAIN:  Yes, me.  Said they had offered it to

everybody and didn't think they could do worse.  Welcome, stranger.

BISHOP WILLIAM MONTGOMERY BROWN:  Is God here?

MARK TWAIN:  There he is.

BISHOP BROWN:  Well, well.  And I denied it.

INGERSOLL:  Denied what?

BISHOP BROWN:  I am Bishop William Montgomery Brown.  I was tried for heresy by the Protestant Episcopal Church in the United States of America.

INGERSOLL:  You must have showed gleams of intelligence.

SOCRATES:  What is heresy?

INGERSOLL:  It's a sport which was very popular with the church in the Middle Ages.  The hounds were churchmen and the victims were burned.

MARK TWAIN:  A religious barbecue.

INGERSOLL:  Heresy is what you were poisoned for, Socrates.  Not believing in the gods as given by the priests, the ruling priests.

SOCRATES:  But priests are men, like ourselves.  Which is better—beliefs or good acts?

INGERSOLL:  I say good acts.

SOCRATES:  And what do you say, Mark?

MARK TWAIN:  I say good acts.  Anybody can talk —it dies on the wind.

SOCRATES:  And are you a priest?

BISHOP BROWN:  I was, but was expelled, cast out.

SOCRATES:  What do you say—is it better to say good words and not live them, or to live a good life without words?

BISHOP BROWN:  A good life is better.  It speaks louder than words.

SOCRATES: Then if you and I lived good lives, though we did not believe all things taught by the priests, ought we not to have been praised rather than condemned?

BISHOP BROWN: I think so.

SOCRATES: I have always thought so. I thought instead of poison they should have given me a pension from the treasury as the Great Questioner, teaching men to think.

MARK TWAIN: Men—dung.

INGERSOLL: Compel men to think and they will hate you. What was your heresy?

BISHOP BROWN: I said "Banish the gods from the skies and capitalism from the earth."

PAINE: Ah! Ha! Capitalism from the earth. That indeed is heresy. The churches can spare their gods, but not their rich men.

MARK TWAIN: But what has capitalism to do with the church?

PAINE: Everything; the church is capitalism. No, no, my reverend bishop, you may deny the gods but hands off capitalism.

BISHOP BROWN: You must understand I did not deny a great power beyond our knowledge. I did not deny the true human divinity of the poet-philosopher, Jesus Christ, as man born of woman; filled with the holy ghost—the spirit of love and forgiveness.

INGERSOLL: What did you deny?

BISHOP BROWN: I denied miracles. I denied the virgin birth.

INGERSOLL: Why, you couldn't stay in any church and deny miracles. Miracles are the bowels of the church. The virgin birth is the very test of qualification for the church.

PAINE:    True.    If you can swallow the virgin birth you can swallow anything.

SOCRATES:    But what have these beliefs to do with good living?    My friend, did you live a good life?

BISHOP BROWN:    I tried to.    I tried to ease the burdens of men.    I spoke for the oppressed and I wanted socialism.

SOCRATES:    What is that?

PAINE:    O, that's to have the important things of the planet and of society,—the mines, forests, waters, railroads, banks, etc.,—held by the state for the common good.

SOCRATES:    O, Plato.    But if administered for the common good, would not all share in the benefit?

INGERSOLL:    That is the trouble.    But really this man did not play the game according to rule.    A good life has nothing to do with it; in fact, makes it worse.

SOCRATES:    Do you not admit that goodness is the highest aim of life and the highest goodness is——

INGERSOLL:    Now, Socrates, I am not going to admit anything.    If I do I am lost, and I insist the Protestant Episcopal Church and so on——

BISHOP BROWN:    Excuse me; in the United States of of America——

INGERSOLL:    Yes.    And so on.    I insist that this and-so-on was perfectly justified in expelling this soul from the club.

BISHOP BROWN:    From the church.

INGERSOLL:    Yes.    Now you joined that club under its constitution and by-laws didn't you?

BISHOP BROWN:    What club?

INGERSOLL:    This Protestant Episcopal and-so-on. And these club laws declared that the Bible was the revealed word of God—our tall friend over there.    That if he did not chisel the tablets or write the words himself, he at least dictated them to his stenographers. Isn't that so?

BISHOP BROWN:   O, no.  Nobody now believes anything so crude as that.

INGERSOLL:   Come, my friend, you must be fair to the and-so-on.  Doesn't your church declare the Jew Bible is the revealed word of the universal God?

BISHOP BROWN:   O, not those foolish myths and miracles of a superstitious childish age.  I reject those, of course; so does every other churchman.

INGERSOLL:   Ah, but they are not socialists.  Now in three words, according to your club, or church, call it what you like—Is the Hebrew Bible the revealed word of the general God, or is it not?

BISHOP BROWN:   Yes, according to the church it is, but only as the spirit of God speaks through men.

INGERSOLL:   Through Buddha or Socrates here, or Shakespeare?

BISHOP BROWN:   Yes, I think so.

INGERSOLL:   That is not the point.  Never mind what you think.  You have been expelled for what you think.  Does your club, the and-so-on, think Buddha a messenger of God, and his scriptures the holy scriptures—the revealed word of God?

BISHOP BROWN:   No. The church would not accept Buddha and Buddhism.

INGERSOLL:   But if the Jew Bible be God's special and only revelation to the whole world for eternal generations, mustn't you accept it all?  Who is going to edit it, rewrite it?  Does your church single out portions to be accepted as the word of God, or must all be accepted?

BISHOP BROWN: O, in theory the whole book, I suppose, but nobody does.

INGERSOLL: Never mind what they do. The club's constitution requires the Old and the New Testaments to be accepted, doesn't it?

BISHOP BROWN: By club you mean church? Well, yes, theroretically the church dogmas do, but no one does.

INGERSOLL: Never mind. The others are not socialists. So you have to believe the earth is flat, and the sun goes around the earth, and once the sun stood still; though we know the earth is round and couldn't stand still without smashing the universe, and the earth goes 'round the sun, and the sun never has stood still. So we come down to the miracles of raising the dead; the loaves and fishes and the virgin birth.

BISHOP BROWN: But I tell you nobody believes these impossible tales now, not even in the church.

SOCRATES: Are all these things necessary to a good life?

INGERSOLL: Socrates, a good life has nothing whatever to do with theology, nor theology with a good life. We are discussing theology. The point is: the reverend bishop here joined a club which by its constitution and by-laws says these things are God's truth, all of them—Noah's cruise and Jonah's, Shadrac's furnace and Joshua's immovable sun, and that Christ was born of a virgin—and the by-laws of the club say that no one can "belong" who does not believe all these things. So he joins, and says he believes. He swallows hook, line, and sinker. If the club says the moon is green cheese, and he joins, it is green cheese for him. If he changes his opinion and grows wiser, he must leave the club. The club hasn't changed; the church never changes; and if he won't leave willingly, the club has a perfect right to throw him out.

SOCRATES: But he is a good man.

INGERSOLL: Socrates, that has nothing to do with it. He breaks the laws of his club. When he joined he swore to green cheese, and green cheese it must be for him or he must quit.

SOCRATES: But to believe these foolish myths has nothing to do with a good life.

INGERSOLL: I tell you, Socrates, a good life has nothing to do with the church. It's a game according to fixed rules, and he won't play according to rule.

BISHOP BROWN: But I tell you nobody else in the church believes. O, some may believe in the virgin birth in a hazy, mystic, symbolic way.

RABELAIS: Birth is not hazy—birth is not symbolic——

THE VIRGIN MARY: Birth is terrible.

VOLTAIRE: It is—to bear or to be born.

BISHOP BROWN: Many clergymen do not believe in the virgin birth.

THE VIRGIN MARY: What is that?

VOLTAIRE: Madame, you should know.

THE VIRGIN MARY: No, I do not know.

RABELAIS: Holy Mother, virgin birth is for a maid to give birth to a child without any assistance.

THE VIRGIN MARY: Many women have children without help.

VOLTAIRE: He means without help in the creation of the child.

RABELAIS: Not even of a man.

THE VIRGIN MARY: But that is blasphemous. That denies God's law of life.

(GOD *and* JESUS *approach.*)

GOD: Robert, my all-hearing ear has heard you and you seem to be taking my place.

INGERSOLL: We all try to, Lord. This newcomer is the latest victim. A club he belongs to on earth has expelled him for breaking its by-laws.

GOD: The laws of men are made to be broken, as bands about a growing tree. My laws, which are eternal, are not laws, but conditions, which all are free to break, but they must pay the penalty, and I myself cannot stay the penalty or the harmony of the universe would be broken. I know neither anger, malice, mercy, or pardon. What was this law our new friend broke?

INGERSOLL: The rule of the club was that he must believe that you wrote the Jew's Bible.

GOD: The scoundrels. Who says I wrote it?

INGERSOLL: His club says so.

GOD: What club?

BISHOP BROWN: The Protestant Episcopal Church in the United States of America.

INGERSOLL: And so on.

GOD: Don't they give me credit for any cosmic quality? I might admit the poetry, but can't they see I am cosmic, of no age or people?

INGERSOLL: They can't. They would have to have brains.

GOD: Well, after all, it is not important what one believes, or rather, says he believes. It is what one does.

SOCRATES: I said so.

INGERSOLL: So they expelled him.

GOD: He should be glad. The expelled are always freed.

INGERSOLL: There are quite a number of things one must believe to belong to this Protestant and-so-on.

Christ dying, going to hell, resurrecting, going to heaven, and that he was born of a virgin.

GOD: How insulting. My son, did you ever hear of these derogatory tales and this Protestant and-so-on?

JESUS: Never, Father.

GOD: I think the most insultingly stupid of all is that you were born of a virgin. As if I would set aside my first great fundamental law just to disgrace you. Well, I couldn't. I cannot break the established universal conditions. They are I—I am they.

BISHOP BROWN: It's all over now, and I'm glad. I believed in Jesus as a man born as we all are, out of the great life mystery, but a man above us all, our brother showing us the path. I believed in his manhood and his divine spirit, to emulate which we all should strive, but I did not believe in you.

GOD: In me?

BISHOP BROWN: Yes. I did not believe in a personal God at all.

GOD: Ah, my friend, am I personal? Could I be personal and cosmic? Perhaps you were right, and this you now speak with may be but a single apparition of the vast unknown, a momentary phantom of eternity, as on earth a drop of dew is brought from the invisible to the top of a blade of grass.

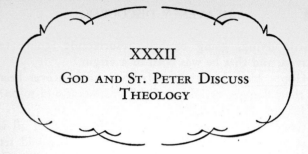

# XXXII

## GOD AND ST. PETER DISCUSS THEOLOGY

(GOD *is sitting on the Jasper Stairs of the First Terrace, swinging a* CHERUB *on his toe.*)

(GABRIEL *comes in.*)

GOD: Gabriel, how is Satan?

GABRIEL: Much better.

GOD: That's good. We need him. Where is Hermes?

GABRIEL: Gone to the games.

GOD: What games?

GABRIEL: The ball games.

GOD: Oh! That accounts for the shower of shooting stars.

GABRIEL: Yes, sir.

GOD: Blow for Peter.

GABRIEL: Yes, sir.

(GABRIEL *goes out.*)

GOD: Well, child, I guess we'll have to stop and attend to business.

CHERUB: I want to play.

GOD: We can't play all the time. You mustn't forget I have the universe on my hands.

CHERUB: Ride me some more.

GOD: Not now. I have my work to do.

CHERUB: Give me a toy.

GOD: Where is that comet I gave you yesterday?

CHERUB: Broke.

GOD: Who broke it?

CHERUB: I did. I pulled off its tail.

GOD: Oh, dear, you children are so destructive. Presently I won't have a comet left fit to be seen. Where did you come from?

CHERUB: From the earth.

GOD: I might have known it. Well, here's a ball, nearly as big as the earth. Don't break it, and don't throw it into any of the stars.

CHERUB: Can I throw it at the earth?

GOD: I don't care. But better ask Jesus. Run along.

(CHERUB *goes out*. ST. PETER *comes in*, VOLTAIRE, RABELAIS, INGERSOLL *and* PAINE *following*.)

ST. PETER: Lord, did you send for me?

GOD: Yes. How are you gentlemen? Peter, I want to have a serious talk with you.

VOLTAIRE: Do we intrude?

GOD: Not at all. Peter, you have been a good saint, according to your light, as you were a good man, but your light is too narrow. You began with the idea that the Jews were the only worth-while people.

VOLTAIRE (*Aside*): It persists—with the Jews.

ST. PETER: Jesus himself said not to bother with other peoples, only to seek the lost sheep of Israel.

GOD: Listen, Peter. You know as well as I do there was not a word of Christ's taken down or written for nearly a hundred years after he was executed as an obscure criminal, and what was then written was filled with a hundred years of imaginings, ideas, and superstitions of many priests and other men. A lot of devils, threats, promises, miracles, contrary to my own laws:

stuff pleasing to the childish minds of an ignorant and credulous people.

VOLTAIRE (*Aside*): I am glad we came.

INGERSOLL (*Aside*): Great.

PAINE (*Aside*): Common sense.

GOD: Then you got the idea that heaven, that is, truth, is only for Christians, and only Christians can enter that vast abode.

INGERSOLL (*Aside*): That idea persists with Christians.

GOD: It's too narrow an idea, Peter. It would disgrace any god. There are many roads to heaven.

VOLTAIRE: His patience passeth understanding.

ST. PETER: But Jesus said so. Jesus said those who believe in him shall inherit life eternal, but those who reject him shall be cast into outer darkness where is wailing and gnashing of teeth.

GOD: No, no. He never said anything of the kind. Why, what kind of a son of mine would he be to teach love and forgiveness as the only truth and salvation, yet visit hell fire on the poor people born into unbelief? That would be more savage than I ever was in my youthful Jehovah days.

VOLTAIRE (*Aside*): How well he remembers.

GOD: What chance is there of such muddled handed-down traditions of childish congregations being an exact report of the words of my son? What you may take and believe are his life and the great, simple, spiritual truths—and that they who believe in these shall live, and they who reject them shall perish of themselves, not by vindictive hell-fire from a god of love.

ST. PETER: Yes.

GOD: That is true. They who believe in love, brotherhood, peace, and forgiveness shall live, and those who believe in hate, revenge, and war shall perish. They who live by the sword shall perish by the sword. That's true—that's my own eternal principle. Love is the constructive, living force; hate the destroying, deathly force. It doesn't mean that nobody shall come to heaven who does not believe my son's special biography as a man, told in these foolish tales. Why, look at him now. So friendly with his elder brothers, Gautama, Socrates, Confucius, and Lao-Tze, over there, who also taught love and forgiveness. Gautama said, "Refuse not food and shelter to your enemy, for the tree refuses not its shade to the axman at its root." And Confucius—"Do not to any man what you would not have done to you." And Socrates—"The good man will not return evil for evil, for then he is no longer good, but no better than the evil man. The good man will return good for evil, for good is always the same and does not change with conditions." Good for evil—this is my own eternal principle.

St. Peter: Can a man be good and reject Jesus as your only begotten son, the savior of mankind?

God: Can he be good? Look about you? Do not be childish, Peter. My sons are many. They sparkle through the ages. Whoever gives his life to teaching love instead of hate is my son. Can a man be bad who believes and does all that Jesus taught, though he never heard of Jesus? Can a man be bad who lives love and forgiveness, brotherhood and peace, yet who cannot believe those childish, impossible tales—virgin birth, miracles, resurrections; all against my own changeless laws?

St. Peter: Not bad, but an unbeliever.

God: Belief is in the doing. That's where the Christians fail; not all the empty professions of their

faith are worth anything against their evil works—
war, hate, poverty. Listen. All good men and women are my children immaculately conceived by virgins, the pure in heart, and through me, the Father,
infinite love. No more of this. Heaven is not a ten-
acre lot, and the religion of love is not kept in a burg-
lar-proof safe, of which you hold the key.

VOLTAIRE: Bravo, bravo! I wish you had said this
to him a thousand years ago.

GOD: A thousand years are but a watch in the
night. I have been patient with you, Peter, because
you are a fisherman. I know the fisherman's soul, how
patiently he waits for a bite, and the thrill when he
feels he has hooked his fish. I have allowed you to
fish at this gate of yours because I felt what a recreation
it was to you.

RABELAIS (*Aside*): God is a good fellow.

GOD: But now you've got to give it up. This toll-
gate idea is too narrow, too absurd. You are making
a circus tent of heaven, and nobody allowed to even
creep under the canvas. And you jingling a bunch of
keys at your waist like a hotel-keeper, or cellarer of a
monastery. Don't you see how childish it all is, and
how unfair?

ST. PETER: But I never started these ideas.

GOD: I know you didn't. I know you didn't, my
good, simple fisherman. I know who started them, and
why they were started. He who holds the keys is a
great power, if they be only the keys of a wine cellar.

RABELAIS: O *mon Dieu. J'ai soif.* Wine cellar.
So cool. So quiet. The meditation of the noble casks.
Saintly bodies, awaiting the perfect resurrection. The
lacery of cobwebs, more beautiful than the cunning of

the sweet, slender fingers of sad-faced young nuns
wrought on surplice and chasuble.  *Hélas! Hélas!* The
Burgundy, the Rhenish——

GOD:  What do you mutter, François?

RABELAIS:  Was I muttering?

GOD:  Yes, like the gurgle of a bottle.

RABELAIS:  *O mon bon Dieu,* you torture me.

GOD:  Torture?  I would not do that.  What relief
do you desire?

RABELAIS:  *O Monseigneur,* Omnipotence, would it
be possible for your kind son to repeat now that little
trick with which he delighted the wedding guests at
Cana?

VOLTAIRE (*Aside*):  Trick?

GOD:  No, François.  This is heaven.

RABELAIS:  *Eheu!*  So it is.  So it is.  *Hélas! Pardonnez-moi.*  Go on.

GOD:  So.  Hereafter, Peter, no walls, no gate, no
keys.  Let heaven be wide open.

INGERSOLL:  Wide open?  How the orthodox will
run around in circles at those fearful words "wide
open."

GOD:  I have no concern for the orthodox.

VOLTAIRE:  It is mutual, Deity.

INGERSOLL:  Puritans believe all good, all growth is
to be accomplished by restraints; by force and punishments.  You, if I understand aright, believe all good
and all bettering must come from growth in freedom?

GOD:  Yes, Robert, and what the Puritans have yet
to learn is that there can be no freedom to be good
without freedom to be bad.  Freedom to rise upward
means freedom to sink downward.  For freedom there
is always a price.  This price the Puritans are not willing to pay.  And so they pay the higher price—they

choke the human will, strangle the human soul, delay the future. They interfere with my cosmic law for the vast majority in order to save a few unfortunates who cannot save themselves. These, I myself would not save—for my law of self-struggle in freedom must not be broken. I am consistent. I am always willing to pay my own price for freedom; extinction of the unfit that the strong-souled and strong-bodied may grow and increase.

PAINE:  Freedom is life.

GOD:  And death. That's the way the forest lives and grows, that's the way man came up from the ocean slime. Freedom is my law of life; immutable as my law of gravity for matter.

RABELAIS:  *Sic itur ad astra.*

PAINE:  No hope without it.

INGERSOLL:  No growth without it.

VOLTAIRE:  Growth by education, not by force. Free thought, free speech, free everything.

PAINE:  Freedom, the very air by which we live.

INGERSOLL:  The nourishment by which we grow.

GOD:  Do you hear, Peter? These are my children, too. Throw open heaven wide and let the upward struggle and the downward fall continue here also.

ST. PETER: But you yourself decreed that those who died in war, and none of the stupid might come in.

GOD:  The stupid never can come in. It needs no notes to keep them out.

ST. PETER:  What shall I do? My occupation gone.

GOD:  You might convert your church back to Christ. Do you realize, Peter, that your church in all these years has never once led human thought or stood for any rebellion toward freedom and progress, but has steadily supported power, tryanny, authority, the old against the new, and has tried to shut out every new ray of light? Do you realize that your church is founded on ignorance, superstition, and blind obedience, that it puts the mythologies of the Jews, old and new, above the living truth voiced by me in the tongues of rocks, the sea, the golden pollen of plants, the egg and the spark? These and such as these are the Book of Life which I myself have written. The church puts the authority of the church above all. Go, my worthy fisherman, cast your hook into the depths of your own church and may you have good luck; but as for the world at large, hang up your nets, wind up your lines, and throw away your bait; cast down your useless keys. Let all come in. Be sure if heaven is free, only the fit can stay.

INGERSOLL: And we need them.

GOD: I am ashamed that Satan, who is getting well, they say, should see how poor we are. What an absurd idea that I should act by men as my agents and give men power to say who shall enter heaven. Absurd and insulting. Go take the gate from off its hinges. Lay it flat. And put a notice on the wall: "Free. All welcome. No questions asked." Sign it yourself.

(ST. PETER *goes out*)

RABELAIS: *Le pauvre Pierre, il est triste.*

GOD: Yes, I know. A fisherman will wait eternity, always hoping for a bite.

PAINE: Omnipotence, we are going off to talk awhile of freedom.

GOD: Do so. And if you find it ever has worked ill or lack of it has ever worked for good, come let me know.

(*All but* GOD *go out.* CHILD ANGEL *comes in.*)
Where is that ball I gave you?

CHILD ANGEL:   I threw it at the earth.

GOD:   Did you ask Jesus?

CHILD ANGEL:   You said you didn't care.   I missed it anyway.

GOD:   That's a pity.

CHILD ANGEL:   Give me another ride.

GOD:   Well, get on my toe.

# XXXIII
## Joan of Arc, Heretic and Saint

(God *sits on his throne, meditating.* Jesus *is conversing with* Buddha. Voltaire *and* Rabelais *are playing chess.* Joan of Arc *and* Mark Twain *are watching them.*)

RABELAIS: Check.

VOLTAIRE: I became used to that below.

RABELAIS: No. No, brother fox, always you saved your tail.

VOLTAIRE: Always by lies.

RABELAIS: Speak not disrespectfully of lies. How could kings and governments exist without them. No war could be made without lies. Lies, the clever tools of diplomats. No institution on earth exists without lies.

VOLTAIRE: Not even the church?

RABELAIS: Not even the church—holy lies dedicated to the greater glory of God.

VOLTAIRE: To the greater glory of God?

RABELAIS: Exactly. O, *mon ami,* do you not in this ethereal state miss a throat? The friendly gullet? The welcoming weazand—the kindly and receptive maw? The dear, good gustatory canal of gourmandizing?

VOLTAIRE: Hush, Reverend Father—the throat is of the flesh.

RABELAIS: Alas, I know it. And we live in the spirit—*in spiritu sancto,* and die in the flesh. Nevertheless, I miss just now the pleasant death of a flagon of Burgundy down the throat.

GOD: Joan.

JOAN OF ARC: Lord.

GOD: Come here, Joan. So, now you are a saint.

JOAN: I am what I always was.

GOD: You think so, but if my unforgetting, neverfailing memory serves me correctly, you were burned as a witch—a heretic, an evil thing in league with the devil.

JOAN: I was the same then as now.

GOD: No, Joan. Then you were a very diabolical thing in league with my interesting friend, Satan, whom your accusers were pleased to call the enemy of mankind.

VOLTAIRE: As if man needed any enemy but himself.

GOD (*To* VOLTAIRE): You are an observer. And, now, Joan, you are a saint.

RABELAIS (*Aside, to* VOLTAIRE): Do you not think, *mon ami,* that God on nearer acquaintance becomes very interesting?

VOLTAIRE (*Aside*): He has been much maligned.

RABELAIS (*Aside*): He has humor and sympathy— great sympathy.

VOLTAIRE (*Aside*): And intelligence. Not at all the malicious, revengeful, stupid fellow his agents have represented. Let us discuss *La Pucelle* with him. (*To* GOD) Omnipotence and Omniscience, one must never forget she was burned by the English.

GOD: She does not care who burned her. But **one**

may be permitted to recall that the French turned her over to the English for burning.

VOLTAIRE: Hm. Well, hardly the French — the Burgundians.

RABELAIS: Ha! Burgundy, Burgundy—O, for a throat and a glass,—a flask—a cask from *le Côte d' Or*. Rubies and violets. Heaven indeed would be——

GOD: Do not mutter so, François. Well, she was burned.

VOLTAIRE: *Hélas* It seems so.

GOD: And we may be permitted to remember that she was tried, condemned, and sentenced by the church. O Peter, Peter. By the way, where is Peter?

VOLTAIRE: Having no gate and no keys he has gone fishing.

GOD: The man is the father of the saint. Well.

RABELAIS: *Pardon, Monseigneur.* The church has never shed blood, has never taken life. It has been true to the divine mercy of Christ. It has always stopped with judgment and for the actual slaying has handed the victim over to the secular arm.

GOD: Such is the divine mercy of Christ. Ah, Doctor, you are a humorist. What would heaven be without humorists?

VOLTAIRE: And poets.

GOD: Yes, the poets. My son, Jesus, the supreme poet. You say the church only gives judgment and leaves another to strike the blow. I suppose the poor wretch who lighted the faggots about this girl was the real executioner.

RABELAIS: Exactly. Now you begin to understand.

GOD: I have never held the knife guilty nor the hand that struck, but only the will that moved them.

VOLTAIRE (*Aside*): God is a funny fellow.

RABELAIS: Ah, *Monseigneur.* You miss the very meat of the matter—she was not tried by the church, but by the Holy Office of Inquisition.

VOLTAIRE: A purely secular body. Eh, *mon père?*

RABELAIS: Not so. Chess players are not always to be trusted in matters of the church. No. Not a secular body, yet not the church itself.

VOLTAIRE: Interesting.

GOD: Explain.

RABELAIS: The Holy Office, it is true, is an arm of the church—a tribunal of the church—and has exclusive jurisdiction—in spiritual matters and matters of faith.

GOD: Faith in whom?

RABELAIS: In the church.

GOD: Well?

RABELAIS: But the Office of Inquisition is not the church itself.

GOD: Why do you squirm, Voltaire?

VOLTAIRE: Nothing. Only an earthly reminiscence. Trying to put my finger on a flea.

GOD: Go on, François.

RABELAIS: I say the Holy Office, though an arm of the church, is not and was not the church itself.

VOLTAIRE: Have a care, dear chess player—*fecit per alium fecit per se.*

RABELAIS: Yes, I know. What is done through another is the same as if done by ourselves. But—but—and it is a big "but." But that is as to powers which can be delegated and as to an act within the scope of those powers. Now the church in its last essence or quintessence is the Holy Father alone.

GOD: I am in the dark.

RABELAIS: *Fiat lux.* Your beloved son, Jesus

Christ, laid his hands in apostolic blessing on Peter—on Peter alone and none other—mark that, only on Peter, creating him his successor, his vice-gerent **on** earth. This divine essence cannot be dissipated. It remained in Peter alone—he alone was the successor to Jesus—and so it remains *saecula saeculorum*, forever and ever in the Holy Father, sole and single as the successor to Peter, the successor to Christ. *Spiritus solus in corpore solo.* The Pope has no ability to pass it or any portion of it out of himself into others or any other —not so much as the hair of a flea: that would be an usurpation of Christ. I hope I have your attention.

GOD: You certainly have. Go on.

RABELAIS: The conclusion is—you will see if you think a minute that the Holy Father alone is the vicar of Christ, so that he alone is the church and as the divine virtue cannot be delegated, no act, thought, or word is that of the church save only that of the Holy Father himself.

VOLTAIRE: Q. E. D.

RABELAIS: Exactly.

GOD: If, then, an arm of the church, say this Inquisition, errs, it is not the error of the church; but if it does not err, then it is the act of the church?

RABELAIS: Exactly.

VOLTAIRE: Convenient.

RABELAIS: Now I hope you begin to understand.

GOD: Well, I fear I do not understand how the Holy Father could find any business nearer to Christ than saving wretches from suffering and a cruel death.

RABELAIS: But, Omnipotence, the Holy Father is not only a spiritual sovereign—head of that powerful institution, the church, but is also a temporal sovereign, one of the monarchs of the earth, and though in these later days his earthly territory has diminished, he still claims the right of an earthly monarch to sit in the councils of kings.

GOD:   To save a soul or a body from torture he had better neglect the councils of kings, and follow the bleeding footsteps of my son.

RABELAIS: Then what would become of the church?

GOD:   Friend François, there is no human institution I could not dispense with and feel the better for the loss.

RABELAIS:   Not the church?

GOD:   Perhaps easiest of all.

RABELAIS:   But it is not a human institution.

GOD:   Perhaps most of all.   Is it not of men, by men, for men?   Perhaps more full of intolerance and error than any other.

RABELAIS:   O Omnipotence; really, I must insist there you are completely wrong.   Could your son, Jesus, partaker of your own divine perfection, err? Impossible.   Then by the logic of theology, neither can his successors err—heirs to that divine perfection.   The Popes are not only partakers of his divinity, through Peter and the apostolic blessing, but are vessels into which all his divinity has been poured.   Acting as a temporal sovereign in matters of the earth, the Pope is man and is liable to err, as are we all.   But, acting as the spiritual sovereign, successor to Peter, vicar of Christ, he cannot err.   For Christ cannot err and the Pope is Christ on earth.

VOLTAIRE:   Red wine and white from the same bottle.

RABELAIS:   It can be done with the help of God.

GOD:   When did the church—that is the Popes—discover this divine property?

RABELAIS: The dogma——

GOD: The what?

RABELAIS: Dogma.

GOD: What is that?

RABELAIS: Surely, Omniscience, you who know all things know that a dogma is a dogma.

GOD: I was not sure. Go on.

RABELAIS: The dogma was only recently discovered, but has not the diamond found today among gravel existed always from the very beginning? So also this divine property of infallibility has always existed in the Popes from and through Peter. To think otherwise is absurd. You cannot begin in the middle of the sausage——

VOLTAIRE (*Aside*): O his eternal sausages!

RABELAIS:—but it must be a continuous chain, link by link, from the beginning.

VOLTAIRE: *Gardez, Maître François,* "sausages"—"continuous chain"—"link by link"—you will end where the devils did, in the swine.

GOD: So then the Pope of Joan's day was infallible and could not err.

RABELAIS: In things of the church—infallible; he could not err.

VOLTAIRE: Fortunate man.

RABELAIS: Not man—not man at all. My chess comrade here fails to draw the distinction.

GOD: So do I, François.

RABELAIS: One moment, Omniscience, and I will make it clear, if you can comprehend the simplest principles of theology—only one moment.

GOD: Take eternity, Doctor. I have already told you that you were admitted here for your humor.

RABELAIS: Ah, *Monseigneur*, life, death, and even this charming retreat are all comedies.

GOD: By the way, François, have you ever been sainted?

RABELAIS: Not yet, Omnipotence.

GOD: I suppose these things sometimes drag.

RABELAIS: They do, Omniscience, they do. When I said the Pope cannot err in things spiritual, but is infallible, my chess comrade exclaimed "fortunate man," which shows that he does not understand. I will explain.

VOLTAIRE: We live in hope.

RABELAIS: As *man*, acting as *man*, the Pope, like the rest of humanity, is liable to err.

VOLTAIRE (*Aside*): Seems reasonable.

RABELAIS: But as Pope, acting as Peter's successor, in things spiritual—never. Impossible. He cannot err.

VOLTAIRE: Ah! Red and white wine in the same bottle.

RABELAIS: No. He cannot err, not by so much as the length, breadth, or thickness of the eye-lash of a fly. I swear by the sacred tail of my sacred mule— *Pardonnez-moi, Monseigneur*—if that intelligent fellow-sufferer on earth were to be made Pope his very bray would be infallible——

VOLTAIRE: Provided, of course, that he brayed in matters spiritual, acting as——

RABELAIS: Exactly; acting as successor to Peter and not as mortal mule.

GOD: Very interesting to me. I have made so many mistakes myself. Man, for example. But, François, if the Pope of Joan's day was not only Christ's representative on earth, but also was lifted out of human fallibility and could not err, then I insist he should have been where Christ himself would have been—at the stake, by the faggots to save this child from torture.

JOAN:   I breathed in flames.   It was terrible.

GOD:   One who has such powers loses great opportunities if he fails to act, himself.

RABELAIS:   He cannot attend to everything in person.   You know how that is yourself, Omnipotence.

GOD:   I attend to nothing—I made my conditions in the beginning—happy he who knows them—and upon the violator they work their unrelenting will.   I myself neither stretch out a hand to save nor do I follow after to wreak hate.

RABELAIS:   The church does not hate, Omniscience.

GOD:   I have said it.   Hate—infallible!

RABELAIS:   But not omniscient, not omnipotent.

GOD:   Why not?   They should go together.

VOLTAIRE (*Aside*): The comedy is at its height.

GOD:   Listen.   Joan is a saint of the church?

RABELAIS:   Without doubt.

GOD:   She was burned as witch and heretic in league with the devil.

RABELAIS:   I am afraid so.

GOD:   The Pope of that time was infallible?

RABELAIS:   In things of the church.

VOLTAIRE (*Aside*):   The red wine.

GOD:   Yes.   And heresy and correspondence with the devil were things of the church?

RABELAIS:   I see, Omniscience, you have caught the idea.

GOD:   So if the Pope of her day had sat in Joan's trial his infallibility would have known her for a saint, not a heretic and witch, and she would not have been burned.

RABELAIS: Inevitably.

GOD: And she would have been sainted at once.

RABELAIS: May I explain in behalf of the church?

GOD: The church allows the devil an advocate. Shall I be less civil to the church?

RABELAIS: Joan most certainly was a saint at the time of her translation.

VOLTAIRE (*Aside*): By fire.

RABELAIS: And she has now been beatified by the Pope acting as——

VOLTAIRE: Saint-maker.

RABELAIS: No. No. Say rather detector. Saints make themselves by their acts of God. But whether, if the Pope of her day had sat as her judge, she would have been at once beatified, I cannot say. That is a matter for the College to determine.

GOD: No colleges, Doctor—no holy offices, Doctor. We have here the one infallible, the church in one man. If a saint now she was a saint then.

RABELAIS: It would seem so.

GOD: And she would not have been burned.

RABELAIS: No.

GOD: Then it is a pity the Pope did not act himself.

RABELAIS: He was much absorbed in politics at the time.

GOD: So he was—I remember. Joan, I have good news for you.

JOAN: Yes, Lord.

GOD: If the Pope of your day had attended to his heavenly business rather than his earthly business, you would not have been burned.

JOAN: But I was burned. The fire was hot.

GOD: Burned in error, Joan, in error. The church has apologized and made you a saint.

JOAN: I am what I always was.

GOD: O, no. You came here as the mistress of the devil. Now you are a saint.

JOAN: I was always what I am now. I do not understand.

VOLTAIRE (*Aside*): Stupid girl.

GOD: You can easily understand, child. The Pope is two men—one an earthly Pope, one a spiritual representative on earth of my son. You were tried and condemned by the Holy Office, an arm of the church which was not an arm of the church, while the spiritual Pope was busy with the affairs of the earthly Pope.

JOAN: I do not understand.

GOD: Nor I. Doctor, I never heard any of this from my son.

RABELAIS: *Hélas!* It is one of the griefs of the church that your son never took any interest in theology. He has left that to the fathers of the church —theologians—but after all wretched mortals.

VOLTAIRE: Very wretched.

RABELAIS: *Excusez.* May I be permitted to tell an ancedote which will illustrate the "two-in-one"— the double quality in the same vessel?

VOLTAIRE (*Aside*): The red and white wine in the same flask.

GOD: Go on.

RABELAIS: Ha! If I were in the flesh how dry my throat would be. When I was in Rome with my lord Cardinal Bellay, he and his suite were given audience by the Pope, and His Holiness offered his toe to my lord to be kissed—his suite following after him, except myself, who remained far back because of my exceeding modesty.

VOLTAIRE: Ahem!

RABELAIS:  By reason of my modesty; seeing which one of the Pope's retinue, scowling black as night, asked me why I did not approach the cathedral to kiss the toe of His Holiness.  I answered that I was debating with myself a most serious question.  "What is that," said my scowler, "which is so serious as to keep you from paying your reverence to the toe of His Holiness?"  "Ah," said I, "that is exactly it.  Is the toe being offered in its spiritual or in its temporal capacity?"  "What difference does that make?" said my spy, scowling.  "Is not the toe of His Holiness—his toe?"  To which I replied:  "All the difference between a jug of Normandy cider and a flagon of rich, old Rhenish, smelling of grape leaves and sunshine; between tripe *en mode de Caen* and stewed goat's shank; between a young virgin all rose leaves and honey and a withered old beldame of the Marais in the thieves' quarter near to the church of Notre-Dame; all the difference between earth, heighho, and this delectable place, in short, all the difference in the world."

VOLTAIRE:  Did the spy remain?

RABELAIS:  Yes.  He——

VOLTAIRE:  Fanatic.

RABELAIS:  I said to him:  "For if the toe was being offered as the temporal toe of an earthly sovereign, even I might make bold to kiss it as I would that of my liege lord, His Most Christian Majesty of France, who had a most powerful great toe of his own; but if it was offered as a spiritual toe, clothed in all the sanctity and infallibility of the church, then I know what was so offered to my own lord Cardinal Bellay, a prince of the church and a great lord of France, was not for me, a poor priest in his train, picking up the crumbs that fall from his table, and I was debating with myself what part of his person the Pope might deign to offer me to kiss"—Whereupon Signor Black-Brows fingered his sword, scowling the blacker, and growled to me: "The devil—a toe is a toe." Seeing that he was of the laity and the herd, incapable of understanding the niceties of theology, I desisted, and, going forward, kissed very humbly the holy toe—not once, but twice, for good measure and to cover all points of debate: once as the earthly toe of the temporal prince and once as the celestial toe of the spiritual sovereign—the substance and the spirit.

MARK TWAIN: When the fellow began his theological defense of the dogmas of the church I thought he was serious.

VOLTAIRE: Rabelais serious!

MARK TWAIN: May he never defend my character.

VOLTAIRE: Reverend Doctor, I am interested even though your papal lackey was not—tell me, does the Holy Father use a double bed?

RABELAIS: Scoffer, beware. The church never forgets, never forgives—and its arm is long. The Pope is a eunuch.

VOLTAIRE: Of God.

RABELAIS: O certainly.

VOLTAIRE: The church of Christ never forgets, never forgives? Ah! But truly it seems according to you the Pope is two persons, and should have a double bed. It has been done.

RABELAIS: If you cannot grasp the two-in-one, how can you comprehend the trinity?

VOLTAIRE: I cannot.

RABELAIS: Infidel. So I end as I began, as all things do—the church of Christ has never erred, has

never shed blood or taken life.   How could it and still
be the church of the All-Merciful Jesus?

JESUS:   What is that?

GOD:   Rabelais has been giving me a lesson in
theology.   He says Peter's church did not burn Joan
here—did not condemn her and give her to the English
to be burned—all this was done by men, but your
church was far away—in Rome—at the time.

VOLTAIRE (*Aside*):   In bed with the Pope.

GOD:   He says your church never has erred—never
can err.

JESUS:   O Father, I err daily.   I am mocked of men
—mock me not.   I have no church.   When did I seek
wealth and power, knowing that wealth and power sit
upon the backs of the oppressed?   Was I ever clad in
splendor?   Did I wear robes of office, or wear the sig-
net ring of authority?   Authority—curse of the world.
Did I ever declare with the voice of authority, or make
rules to be obeyed, or proclaim ordinances to be enforced?   When did I seek the great, the rich, the powerful?   Was not my chosen lot with the slave and the
outcast?   The Magdalens were my sisters—I sought the
redemption of men through earnest pleading for righteousness and justice, and I edged not toward the table
of the high priest or the money-changer, nor toward
the centurion with his sword.   Father, did I build a
wall about myself, filled with intervenors, interceders,
and professional attorneys for salvation, or did I fence
myself in a court more webbed with ritual than Sol-
omon's, heavier with gold than Caesar's? I cried aloud:
"Come to me, all ye that are weary and heavy-laden."
When they came did I say "apply unto Peter—see John
—arrange with Luke or Matthew"?   When did I give

anyone power as my agent between me and the sinner? I have no church, Father; I want no church, neither Peter's nor any other—whitened sepulchres, costly and magnificent, but filled with dead men's bones. Their rules, ordinances, and rituals are more to them than the life, their garments more than the message, their symbols more than the truth, the body more than the spirit, and they lust after power. I have been speaking with my brother Buddha. He also is outcast and betrayed. Always the people look at the image and forget the soul, they pray in words which they make to be husks, and fail in the doing which is life. They build great temples, but on the steps are beggars; truth and justice are buried under them. I have no church, Father, no rules, rituals or authority, and yet my churches are as many as there be those who hunger and thirst after righteousness. In them each one is high priest, knowing as much as another and for himself, more. Is it not all simple to know? Hate not, love one another, forgive your enemies, do unto others as ye would that they should do unto you—simple in the understanding, even for children, but hard in the doing. The churches you mock me with have not learned it— no, not one, not a single syllable. The temple into which I will enter is not to be built with hands, but each one may build it in his own soul of the frail material— love—and there will I be with him.

I am tired, my Father, of the things that are said and done in my name. Again I taste the sponge of vinegar, the gall is bitter, and yet again I cry, Father, forgive them—they know not what they do.

GOD: Leave me alone with my son. Gautama, remain with us.

(*The others silently go out.*)

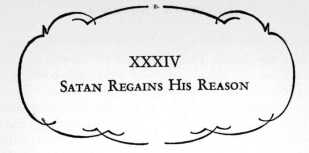

# XXXIV
## Satan Regains His Reason

*(The thousandth terrace of the thousandth plane.*
God *is standing apart, looking afar.* Mary Wollstonecraft, Margaret Fuller, Lucretia Mott,
Emily Dickinson, *and* Sappho; *a group by themselves.* Voltaire, Rabelais, Ingersoll, Paine, Lucretius, *and* Mark Twain; *another group.)*

Margaret Fuller:   What a pity, Sappho, that your
poems were lost.

Sappho:   Why a pity?

Margaret Fuller:   Because though earth and the
cosmos of which it is a part are eternities of beauty, yet
man creates so little of his own out of the eternal
beauty.

Sappho:   What does it matter?

Margaret Fuller:   Is it not a pity to have a jewel
in the hand, feeling its beauty, and lose it?

Sappho:   Jewels there are unknown in mountain
and ocean.   What does it matter to those not knowing?
And jewels are lost, utterly vanished; the owners too
vanish; all is forgotten.   Time and space make a sure
end of all things—make all of no value.   We who
stand on a peak now, higher than once we stood, ought
to see that Time—Time and Space—bring all to conclusion:   this heaven, these stars and Him over yonder

looking afar, His own end foreseeing.  What is Sappho?
A wind-drifted seed of the silver-topped thistle—an
apple blossom, gemming the topmost bough in the sun-
rise torn by a gust, shattered, its petals uselessly scattered
over the grass.  What does it matter?

MARY WOLLSTONECRAFT:  Children cry if they lose
their toys.

MARGARET FULLER:  If a child draws from a wave
a lovely shell but loses it into the sea again, his heart
is wrung, his hour is saddened.

EMILY DICKINSON:  His hour.  The child will pass
—where then his grief?

SAPPHO:  Perhaps because my songs are lost, they
are the better—as things seen of the mind are beautiful beyond the real.

EMILY DICKINSON:  It may be so.

MARY WOLLSTONECRAFT:  Our expectations are
never realized.

LUCRETIA MOTT:  Shall the burden-bearers and the
child-bearers never have their rightful part in the very
world they make?

MARGARET FULLER:  It comes.

(GABRIEL *comes in*.)

GABRIEL:  Omnipotence, Satan has recovered.  He
is well.

GOD:  That is good news.  Now things will move
again with some spirit.  When was this recovery?

GABRIEL: You remember, Omniscience, that he first
began to act queer when the Russian soldiers refused to
fight.

GOD:  Refused to be killed for their masters.  Yes.
Intelligence of the herd then began.

GABRIEL:  Then he had a fainting fit when Wilson——

GOD: Who? I remember. King of that ridiculous country where they pass laws against everything and then break them. Go on.

GABRIEL: He fainted when Wilson gave out his Fourteen Points.

GOD: I remember. I remember. Points. Points. Locations in space without length, breadth, or thickness. Yes. Go on.

GABRIEL: The end came when the Germans proposed an armistice. He was not violent, but fell into a settled melancholy, didn't recognize his best friends —the kings, presidents, prime ministers, generals, statesmen, and diplomats.

GOD: What was that you said finished him.

GABRIEL: Proposal for an armistice.

GOD: Tell Robert and his friends to come here.

(GABRIEL *goes to the group where* INGERSOLL *and the others are conversing, delivers the message, and they approach*). Robert, what is this armistice that drove Satan crazy?

INGERSOLL: O nothing, nothing at all. Merely a proposal to stop fighting.

GOD: Is that all?

INGERSOLL: That's all. A proposal from Germany to end the war, make peace, and each go on about his peaceable business.

GOD: Couldn't they have done all that before they fought?

INGERSOLL: It never has been done.

GOD: Seems foolish. I hate to admit I do not understand one of my own creatures, but man is beyond me. Stupid. Stupid.

PAINE: How can there be reasonable discussion when one country has what another wants, and it must be taken by force and resisted by force. You can't have discussion between two hungry dogs with a juicy piece of meat between them.

GOD: So war comes down to that, does it? Well. It is more stupid than I thought. Go on. The Germans proposed an armistice.

INGERSOLL: Based on the lines of the Fourteen Points.

GOD: Now, Robert, I am the supreme mathematician of the universe. You can't have a line determined by one point. It takes at least two.

INGERSOLL: But they had fourteen.

GOD: I see. I see. They could make any curve they wanted.

INGERSOLL: Curves? Well. Stop. Look. Listen. You ought to see the peace treaty that followed.

GOD: So that is what gave my friend nervous prostration?

INGERSOLL: No. I don't think it was. It may have been a last straw, but Satan was really broken down by overwork.

GOD: Overwork?

INGERSOLL: Yes, the Great War to end war; for democracy, brotherhood, and the salvation of the world.

PAINE: The devil has not had so much to do since the creation.

SOCRATES: Greece died of its wars.

LUCRETIUS: Rome died of its wars.

GOD: But everything was coming his way.

INGERSOLL: That's it. He was overwhelmed with prosperity, overburdened with responsibility, and one foolish little gesture overcame him. If he had only waited.

GOD: Well, what cured him?

GABRIEL: We gave him a radio set to keep in touch with the earth. He said the earth was his only hope. When he heard the actual terms of the armistice the Germans were forced to sign, he looked up; began to take notice. When the French imperial press broke loose, his eyes cleared, he smiled. When the English and United States jingoes began to shout and rave, he became cheerful, alert. And when the news came that a peace treaty was being prepared at Paris itself, Versailles—dictated by Clemenceau and Lloyd George, with the flattered Wilson sitting in—he leaped from his couch, threw off his wrapper, kicked his slippers into space, narrowly missing an asteroid, and shouted: "It is all right. Give me my spear. Hell has broke loose again."

GOD: He's right. There is nothing so hellish as a treaty of peace. War is plain war—but a treaty of peace is war in disguise.

LUCRETIUS: I have seen Roman triumphs.

SOCRATES: And I Athenian.

GABRIEL: In an instant he was well, cured as if by a miracle.

PAINE: It was a miracle. Christianity was cast into him.

MARK TWAIN: How about the poor swine?

GOD: You must not compare Satan to Christians. Satan never was a hypocrite.

GABRIEL: He wants to see you, Omnipotence.

GOD: Gladly. Gladly. Bring him in. It has been very dull.

(GABRIEL *goes out.* JESUS *comes in. The women approach.*)

My son, Satan has recovered.

JESUS: I am glad. We are not so far apart.

LUCRETIA MOTT: Not so far apart? He, Prince of Darkness, war, destruction; you, the Prince of Peace?

JESUS: He is honest, courageous. So, I hope, am I. We both believe the divine principle is freedom. The free soul working out its own salvation or its own destruction. We talked much together in his lucid periods. Here he comes.

(GABRIEL *comes in with* SATAN.)

SATAN: Hail, Omnipotence, Omniscience, Jehovah, Lord, God Almighty—Hosanna, Halleluja, Glory in the Highest. If I have omitted anything of the heavenly etiquette, pardon me; my memory is still a little shattered.

GOD: Welcome, my friend. We have missed you. Heaven has been a little tedious without you.

VOLTAIRE: *C'est vrai.*

MARK TWAIN: Dull as a church in a rich rigging, and deserted as a placer camp a year after the pay dirt gave out—lamps, laughter, clink of glasses and click of roulette wheels all gone, the doors of the gay saloons hanging by rusty hinges or fallen flat, windows broken, grass growing before the door, and a chipmunk on the bar. I want to say with apologies to my friend, Joe Twichell, that heaven has been greatly **overrated.**

GOD: No apologies, second Samuel. Heaven can be dull. That is why I brought you here, and Rabelais and Robert and Voltaire. Satan too is a great humorist. You will like him. Well, my friend, I repeat I am glad you have recovered. I see you are necessary to the cosmos, only another part of me.

SATAN: Thank you. Thank you also for your heavenly hospitality. I want to express my gratitude to Jesus. He has ministered to me when I was sick and it is impossible to say what his visits meant to me. Our discussions were the most illuminating I have ever had. We have much in common.

JESUS: Yes, I told them so.

SATAN: I feel my old strength coming back and I want to return to earth.

GOD: Why to earth?

SATAN: As I survey the cosmos and perceive how all is brought to harmony except upon the earth, I see it is my field. I thought with the awaking intelligence in Russia and the war's fearful lesson to the young that surely war was at an end, that man would come to freedom and brotherhood throughout the globe, and that I must seek newer activities. But in the terms and temper of this Peace Conference I see many future wars—larger, greater, more annihilating. Hate once more has come to rule. My agent Clemenceau is sitting at the table, a gray old tiger cat, meditating spoils and revenge. My agent Lloyd George is standing, legs apart before the fireplace, meditating spoils. Wilson, lost in the fog of his own vanity, is an easy tool. There is no spark of mercy, charity, or forgiveness, much less of brotherhood. All, all is hopeful for a world with newer hates, deeper ignorance, and madder fury. I cannot leave it all to my human agents, the bondtakers, the munition makers, the international bankers, the cabinets, the diplomats—in short, the rulers. They are great powers for evil and anxious to do their best, but I must direct them. When history is written I want all men to know that Clemenceau and Lloyd George stood on either side of me, holding my hand—a trinity—with Wilson behind me, applauding, praying or looking in the glass.

MARGARET FULLER: Do not let him go.

GOD: Why not?

MARGARET FULLER: Do not loose again the Prince of Evil on the earth.

INGERSOLL: What difference does it make? He is not really necessary now. Men are doing hell's work without him.

VOLTAIRE: *Bon, bon,* Robert.

MARY WOLLSTONECRAFT: We women appeal to Jesus.

JESUS: If salvation be of worth, men must gain it by the sweat of their souls—it cannot be handed to them on a golden platter. The sweat of the soul comes from struggle in freedom and is understanding. Let him go.

SATAN: Thanks, my gentle enemy. Through you I see my ultimate defeat; but now——

JESUS: We are not enemies. Only necessary oppositions. We each believe in freedom. Come salvation or damnation, there must be freedom that the soul may survive. Shall I, who said "Forgive your enemies," not be the first to love one who calls himself my enemy? I refuse the word. Go, and out of evil shall come good, if men be wise.

PAINE: Ah, if men be wise.

VOLTAIRE: Vain hope.

LUCRETIUS: What flowers, what fruit, what songs out of the celestial harmony if men were wise. But men are never wise, and so I killed myself. O, who that could be free in large ethereal death would walk the narrow prison-path, whose pavement is sharp flints, whose hedges, thorns?

SOCRATES: Knowledge is all. Understanding, all.

PAINE: Yes. Begin with schools. Let children learn that wars are always for spoils.

SOCRATES: Greed and spoils.

INGERSOLL:  Knowledge is wisdom.

MARK TWAIN:  Not the same, Bob, not the same. Bill Turk, who kept the saloon at Battery and Sacramento, San Francisco, couldn't read, and kept his score with beans—with different colored beans and a six-shooter, but he was wise.  He said to me, "Sam, keep your dust.  Get all you can and keep it.  It will starve you in the desert and sink you on the ocean, but in this rat pit where we are caught it's the whole cheese."

RABELAIS:  *Qu'est-ce que c'est que ça?*  Cheese? *Ah, les fromages de crême.*  Did he say in San Francisco cheese is money?

VOLTAIRE:  No.  No.  He said with money you can buy cheese.

RABELAIS:  *Mon Dieu,* with money you can buy anything.

MARY WOLLSTONECRAFT:  Not brains.

RABELAIS:  *Oui, oui.*  Most certainly brains.

SAPPHO:  Nor love.

VOLTAIRE:  But a good imitation.

EMILY DICKINSON:  Money buys only what can be weighed or measured.  It cannot buy one spiritual treasure.

RABELAIS:  Ah, it will buy wine, the ruby and the golden, which makes for wit, cheer, good-fellowship. Are not these spiritual?

VOLTAIRE:  And sausages.  Eh?

RABELAIS:  *O mon ami—les saucissons, les vins de Bourgogne.*

SATAN:  Good Father François, good Doctor, before we stray too far, let me bring this learned and distinguished company——

INGERSOLL (*Aside*):  That's the way he talks to Wilson.

SATAN: —back to the thought that Jesus and I are not so far apart. Now killing is not so wrong in itself, as you will admit.

MARGARET FULLER: Never.

SATAN: Was not the rebellion that made England a little free, good, though it cut off a king's head; was not the rebellion that made France a little free, good, though it cut off a king's head; was not the Civil War in your United States good in that it set free the slaves?

MARGARET FULLER: It was not fought to free the slaves, but to save the union of states—a political question. The slaves could have been bought free for less. But you speak of rebellions of the people—I speak of "wars" which are never by or for the people.

SATAN: But they are killings and sufferings. Nevertheless you will agree if wars are by a people against their masters, to throw off a yoke, they are good.

INGERSOLL: They are, Margaret, they are. It is a poor way, but stupid rulers seem to force it and if it frees the people it is good. Rebellions are good.

MARK TWAIN: Evolution's growing-pains.

PAINE: Even this Russian rebellion was for freedom, and teaches a lesson. Remember the Soviets and communism whether good or bad are not all there is in the Russian revolution.

SATAN: Then if by wicked wars for spoils I teach the people finally to rebel against their masters, is it not good out of evil? You see Jesus and I are not so far apart. We both promote growth. We are only opposites. Evil is the opposite of good; light is the opposite of darkness. And then suppose they are not opposites, but extremes of the same thing. Darkness and light extremes of the same principle; evil and good the same principle in extremes. Jesus and I extremes of the same thing.

MARY WOLLSTONECRAFT: No. No. Love and hate are extremes as far apart as the poles of the universe, but they are not of the same thing.

SATAN: Excuse me, Madame. It is most interesting to have ladies enter our discussions. Formerly it was not so.

INGERSOLL: And formerly so dull.

SATAN: Very dull. I believe in women.

VOLTAIRE: *Mon Dieu.* You ought to.

SATAN: Yes. Dear little Eve and the others. But let us see. A woman so hates another she gives her poison.

MARGARET FULLER: Why not a man?

SATAN: Very well. A woman so hates a man she gives him poison.

MARGARET FULLER: No, no. I mean, why always a woman to give the poison?

SAPPHO: He is right. The weapon of the weak. Let it go.

SATAN: Very well. She poisons because she hates. A mother gives her child things she knows poison his body, and things she knows poison his soul, because she loves. You see, love and hate do the same thing. Jesus would have wars to cease because he wants peace. I want men to destroy themselves until they cease to be fools. Well, when they cease to be fools we shall have peace. Jesus wants to inoculate men with love; I want to afflict them with hate till they learn love, which is wisdom, but when the end is reached it will be found that love and hate, selfishness and unselfishness are different reactions of the same thing. Wisdom will teach that the highest selfishness is to do unto others as you want them to do to you.

GOD: Satan, you are too smart. You are a diplomat. Go to your Peace Conference. They seem to be doing very well without you, but go.

SATAN: They only seem. Just as with Wilson present they seem to be able to do without you, but really it is not the same. I can put more hell into their work.

MARK TWAIN: Impossible.

SATAN: *Au revoir. Auf Wiedersehen.*

VOLTAIRE (*Laughingly*): Hun.

(SATAN *goes out. The men and women mingle.* JESUS *walks apart.* GOD *looks afar.*)

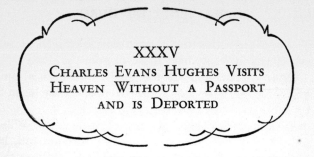

# XXXV
## CHARLES EVANS HUGHES VISITS HEAVEN WITHOUT A PASSPORT AND IS DEPORTED

(GOD *is lying down;* INGERSOLL, RABELAIS, VOLTAIRE, MARK TWAIN *strolling about, chatting.*)

(ST. PETER *comes in.*)

ST. PETER: Where is God?

INGERSOLL: In the heavens and in the earth, from everlasting to everlasting.

ST. PETER: O, no joking. Where is he?

INGERSOLL: There he is.

GOD: What do you want, Peter?

ST. PETER: O Lord, there is a most unusual case at the gate.

GOD: At the gate? Peter, I told you I would not endure this any longer. I will not have a custom-house for heaven.

ST. PETER: Just a moment, Lord. There is no gate. I meant the place where it was. The gate is down, and I have that "Free for all" notice up. I have nothing to do, no credentials to examine, or anything. I can't even fish. So I just sit there and the souls come up, hang around, walk in or walk away. My only occupation now is just to watch the crowd.

GOD: It is hard, I suppose, to drop a habit of nearly two thousand years.

ST. PETER:   Yes, Lord, it is.   When I saw this one I jumped up before I thought and said: "See here, stranger, you can't come in."

GOD:   That was wrong.

ST. PETER:   I'm not so sure, Lord; because this man has not yet died.

GOD: Has not died?  Bring him in.  This is curious.

(ST. PETER *goes out and returns with* CHARLES EVANS HUGHES.)

MARK TWAIN:   Br-r-r.  It is cold.  We miss Satan. He certainly kept the home fires burning.

ST. PETER:   This is the man.

GOD:   They tell me you are not dead.

HUGHES:   O, but I am.   As dead as a salted mackerel.

GOD:   Have you died?

HUGHES:   Not technically—not in the flesh, but politically I am as dead as anyone can be—deader than a door-nail.

GOD:   What is your name?

HUGHES:   Charles Evans Hughes, formerly Secretary of State for the United States.

GOD:   That's on the earth?   Christ's earth?

HUGHES:   Well, yes, it's on the earth.

INGERSOLL:   He's dead all right.  I know the dead ones when I see them.

GOD:   Yes, he really seems dead.

HUGHES:   I am, Lord, I am.  I wouldn't deceive you.  I am a member of John's church.

GOD:   Ah!  John, the Baptist?

HUGHES:   Well, it's the same church.

GOD:   There is a friend of yours here.

HUGHES:   A friend of mine?

GOD:   Lenin, from Russia.

HUGHES: You are mistaken—he is no friend of mine. He favors revolution, rebellion, and wants to abolish the finest system ever evolved by humanity, the Capitalistic System of the Republic of the United States.

GOD: So you think mankind has evolved to the end and can go no further?

HUGHES: Yes, sir. It is perfect. Perhaps some little mistakes in execution, but as a system—perfect. Even you could not better it.

GOD: So at last evolution has come to an end in something. Poor Lenin. Then he has made a mistake?

HUGHES: He certainly has. And we sent over the Root Commission to show those people. But would the Bolshevists take our lesson in liberty? No. They imprisoned people for speaking against Bolshevism. They prohibited free press, broke up printing offices of the hostile Socialists, raided meetings, and sent people into exile for their political opinions. Just because they opposed the government.

MARK TWAIN: Why, that is exactly what the United States is doing.

HUGHES: Certainly not. Speech, press, and drama are absolutely free under the Stars and Stripes.

MARK TWAIN: Never any police interference, never any meetings broken up, nobody ever sent to jail for holding I. W. W. cards?

HUGHES: O, that's different. Anything that threatens our institutions or our morals must be suppressed.

MARK TWAIN: And in Russia free speech threatens Bolshevist institutions. That's all the difference.

INGERSOLL: Tyranny is tyranny, Charles. You're

a poor sport if you want free speech only for your own ideas.

HUGHES: But our ideas are perfect.

MARK TWAIN: Excuse me. The Supreme One over there says he doesn't know himself how anything will work till it's tried, and even he keeps changing.

HUGHES: Well, I know. And besides, this I. W. W. constitution advocated overthrowing the government by force.

PAINE: Shades of Benjamin Franklin, Thomas Jefferson, and George Washington!

INGERSOLL: Bosh. The United States was founded on overthrowing a tyrannous government by force. The United States Constitution guarantees free speech and free press, and that means the right to advocate throwing over the government by force, just as the Declaration itself says. Did these I. W. W. boys our baseball umpire — Kenesaw — Kickshaw—Rickshaw— Mountain Landis sent to jail for the best years of their young lives do any acts of violence?

HUGHES: No.

INGERSOLL: Did they advocate any?

HUGHES: No, but their constitution did.

INGERSOLL: Bosh. They didn't know any more about that constitution than you do about that of the United States.

HUGHES: Sir, who are you?

INGERSOLL: I am Bob Ingersoll.

HUGHES: The atheist?

INGERSOLL: No, sir. The agnostic, the infidel, if you please; the freethinker, free speaker, free everything.

VOLTAIRE: Bravo, Robert.

HUGHES: Very well, sir. I am Charles Evans

Hughes, formerly Secretary of State, and it was my business to know the Constitution of the United States.

MARK TWAIN:   Pity you didn't attend to your business.

HUGHES:   I did, sir, and more.

MARK TWAIN:   I believe you, a great deal more.

INGERSOLL:   By the beard of the prophet.  If you came to trial before the great baseball judge, K. Mountain Landis, and he thought as much of the firebrands in the U. S. Constitution as he did of those in the I. W. W. Constitution, you would not have escaped a twenty-year sentence.

HUGHES:   Who?  Me?  I?

INGERSOLL:   O baptism would not have saved you.

HUGHES:   Me?  I?

INGERSOLL:   Did you not at the request of the Mussolini dictatorship of Italy have Carlo Tresca, editor of *Il Martello*, an Italian paper in New York, arrested because he published an article against the Mussolini tyranny, headed "Down with the Monarchy"?  Was he not arrested at the request of Gelasio Caetani, Mussolini's ambassador in Washington?

HUGHES:   No, sir. I did not. Not personally.  I turned that complaint over to the Post Office Department for action and that department turned it over to the Department of Justice for action and that department arrested the editor.

RABELAIS:   *Mon Dieu.*  It is the papal arm and the secular arm in politics.

INGERSOLL:   Arrested him for a political article agains a foreign government, calling for resistance to a foreign dictatorship.  Since when has the United States begun to pull out of the fire the chestnuts of foreign tyrannies?

HUGHES:   The editor was arrested for publishing a birth-control advertisement.

RABELAIS:   *Mon Dieu—Mon Dieu.*

INGERSOLL:   Come, good baptist.   Why was the State Department, or any department of the government, so interested in birth control?   Was not the accusation changed to "birth control" because to criticize a foreign government could not be made to stick; even to oblige the Italian ambassador and even under the bureaucratic dictatorship to which the United States has descended?

HUGHES:   Well, you'll have to ask the Department of Justice what procedure it adopted and why.

INGERSOLL:   But the indictment was in fact changed from its first intent and the paper was finally suppressed till it cancelled a little three-line birth-control ad.   Isn't that true?

HUGHES:   I believe it is.

MARK TWAIN:   May I ask Charles the Baptist, what is Signor Mussolini's deep interest in American birth control?

VOLTAIRE:   There must be soldiers, perhaps.

MARK TWAIN:   I think, now that women are enfranchised, we should be free to manage our own birth control without suggestions from the Italian ambassador in Washington.

VOLTAIRE:   Perhaps Signor Mussolini or his ambassador has friends with *les femmes sages.*

HUGHES:   But you understand, as you have yourselves admitted, we only changed to birth control when we found we could not gratify Signor Mussolini by suppressing a New York paper on other and political grounds.   We never would have begun with birth control.   We were driven to it.   Having begun, we had to finish by hook and by crook. Also you understand I did not do this myself—I handed it over to the Post Office Department, they in turn to the Department of Justice.

RABELAIS: Another court of the inquisition, another case of the double, no, treble, personality. Very interesting. When *Monsieur Barbegris* turns over a paper to be suppressed by another department, it is all the same as when the church turned over Jeanne d'Arc to the secular arm to be burned. Ah ha! Is it not so? *Très curieux.*

INGERSOLL: Come on, Charles. Why cannot you church people be honest? You say you did not yourself act as tool for Mussolini, but when Count Karolyi asked for leave to enter the United States to see his sick wife, did you not—you, yourself, *in propria persona*—refuse to let him come to her bedside till he had solemnly promised you, yourself, my whiskered friend, that he would neither write nor speak on Hungarian affairs?

HUGHES: Well, you see—the Hungarian government asked me to do this.

PAINE: Shade of Louis Kossuth. Shade of Thomas Jefferson. Shade of Daniel Webster.

MARK TWAIN: Shade of Benedict Arnold.

HUGHES: Count Karolyi had been the head of the radical government that arose from the Hungarian revolution. Then there was a counter-revolution and a government was set up by the reactionaries, the aristocrats, Count Karolyi's own class, many of them his friends, whose great landed estates were being condemned for the common, rebellious peasants under Count Karolyi.

MARK TWAIN: Now that wasn't nice of the Count, was it, Charles? To go back on his own class and yours?

HUGHES: Exactly, and you see the present aristocratic government didn't want any agitation in the United States. Neither did we.

MARK TWAIN: It might stop loans, or even hurt the bankers who had already loaned?

HUGHES: Exactly.

MARK TWAIN: Nice, aristocratic, accommodating Charley, and the Constitution be damned.

INGERSOLL: And free speech in the United States suppressed in the interest of a foreign feudal aristocracy.

LENIN: And he criticises Russia.

MARK TWAIN: O what is a mossy, old constitution between aristocratic boys like Charley and Count Szechenyi.

GOD: What's that? What's that? Did some one sneeze?

INGERSOLL: No, Lord. That's the name of the Hungarian minister who told Charles the Baptist here how America must be governed.

MARK TWAIN: So, the United States is now run by the foreign ministers at Washington, for whom Charles the Baptist acts as secretary.

GOD: Peter, Peter, will you never get over your secret service habits? Why are you sniffing about?

ST. PETER: That's it. That's it. I knew it. I smelled a rat from the first. He has no business here. First, he has never died; and second, he isn't a soul at all—he is an imitation.

GOD: Show him down.

# XXXVI
## England's General Strike

(*The Seventh Plane of Heaven.* God, Jesus, *and* Buddha *talking apart. A Group*—Voltaire, Tom Paine, Rabelais, Robert Ingersoll, Margaret Fuller, *and others. A great buzzing of the Radio.*)

God:  Robert, what is that?

Ingersoll:  Earth is broadcasting an extra: "Great general strike in England—Four million workers walk out—Industries paralyzed—All newspapers suspended."

Voltaire:  That last is something.

Ingersoll:  "Premier Baldwin says it is a revolt against ordered government—Churchill says it is civil war and rebellion."

God:  What's it all about?

Ingersoll:  The coal mine owners want to cut down wages or lengthen work hours of the miners. The miners say they can't live so they strike, and other trades back them up.

God:  Is that all? Where's the rebellion? Where is the civil war and destruction of ordered government in all that? Haven't the miners a right not to work?

Paine:  No, Lord. They are slaves, and slaves have no right to quit work. If they do, it is rebellion and strikes at ordered government.

Voltaire:  Britons never, never, never will be slaves.

PAINE: But they are. The whole working class are slaves everywhere, slaves to those who own the natural resources and the public necessities.

INGERSOLL: What! Thomas! The aristocratic unions of American labor, slaves? The boss officials who violently suppress every effort at freedom in their ranks, slaves?

PAINE: Certainly, and you know it.

INGERSOLL: I do. But they don't. Petty tyrants never do.

PAINE: Wait till the master's shoe pinches, and see how quickly the police, the dogs of the masters, will be at their throats. Just now they are pals. Both aim at monopoly.

VOLTAIRE: The master class is a great sow, swollen with monopoly of all the good things of the earth. Sucking at her teats are the white-collar clerks, the employees, the middle class, and the special privilege labor bosses, who when the starving ones try to take from the sow her place at the trough are the first to defend her lest they too lose their turn at a teat.

PAINE: True. True. The support of the masters is the middle class and the labor bosses. The enemy to a just revolution is the middle class and the labor bosses.

GOD: I see no insoluble problem in England. The remedy is simple. Take the mines from the owners. They did not create the mines—I made them, and made them for all the inhabitants of the earth. Let them be taken for all the people and let the people pay the miners their full wages. Isn't it simple?

PAINE: Simple as getting off a horse's back. Too simple, Omniscience. The people—the middle class and the masters—would rather pay taxes, would rather have bloody revolution.

INGERSOLL: They are mobilizing all the armed forces of England—police, army, navy.

PAINE: How clear it is that it is not the acts of the oppressed which make bloody revolutions, but the attacks on the oppressed by the obstinate masters who refuse to surrender one privilege without bloodshed.

GOD: It is worse than foolish. It is stupid. My son, what were you and Gautama saying just now about the brotherhood of man? Come, let us contemplate infinite space from the heights of heaven.

(*All go out.*)

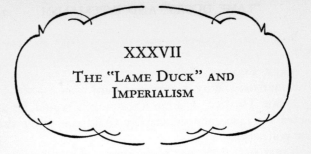

# XXXVII
## THE "LAME DUCK" AND IMPERIALISM

(*A group is watching some young angels at play. JESUS, GAUTAMA, and SOCRATES standing a little apart.*)

MARGARET FULLER:   How beautiful!

RABELAIS:   Ah, Margot!   What I like about heaven is its restfulness combined with stir.

VOLTAIRE:   Eternal change — eternal growth — eternal stimulation—eternal refreshment.

RABELAIS:   No feeling of the slavedriver's whip.

JESUS:   Earth might be so—if men had courage to follow the Golden Rule—bringing leisure to all—peace to all.

GAUTAMA:   The peace of earth is war.

SOCRATES:   Men need leisure to learn wisdom.

GAUTAMA:   Men need to learn that happiness lies not in material things but in the contemplation of spiritual beauty.

MARGARET FULLER:   How beautiful these lovely young spirits at play.

MARK TWAIN:   On earth they would be run in because they are naked.

RABELAIS:   *Qu'est-ce que c'est?* "Run-in"?

VOLTAIRE:   A race.   A speed contest.   Is it not?

MARK TWAIN:   Well, yes.   If you can beat the cop.

RABELAIS:  *Qu'est-ce que c'est?*  "Beat the cop"?
What is cop?

MARK TWAIN:  Policeman.

RABELAIS:  Why do you beat him?

MARK TWAIN:  I mean these angels would be arrested for indecency unless they could run faster than the policeman.

RABELAIS:  I do not understand—*n'importe*

(GOD *comes in attended by* GABRIEL.)

GOD:  How beautiful!  A lovely scene—I am glad to be home.

SOCRATES:  We were just saying man must learn to prefer the general good to selfish power, and learn that such a preference is really a wise selfishness.

GOD:  He must learn the beauty of peace and the peace of beauty.  He thinks he has done much but he has accomplished nothing.

JESUS:  Did you enjoy your holiday, Father?

GOD:  Yes, so much—that I thought on your account I would visit the earth—but as I neared it I saw such a fury of fight; heard such a din and uproar of confusion; such groans, sighs, and sobs of the oppressed that I would not spoil my sense of the harmony of the universe, so I turned away and came home.  Jesus, in less than the million years I promised, your earth brethren will be extinct and I to blame.

JESUS:  
GAUTAMA:  } You?
SOCRATES:  

GOD:  Yes.  Animal I created him but gave him the saving flame of reason, hoping for a beautiful evolution.  Useless—animal he remains.  His saviors, such as you, my sons, cannot save him.  You also he rends.  Well, after all, that is my own law for the unreasoning brute

and brute he remains. How beautiful those spirits.
Where are they from?

GABRIEL: Earth.

GOD: Earth? Earth? What part of earth?

GABRIEL: India and China.

GOD: Oh. Beautiful.

SOCRATES: I want to examine an earthly subject.
We all know that each one, if not compelled by force,
acts as he prefers to act. Now does anyone prefer to
be killed for a stranger?

RABELAIS: *Mon Dieu, non.* Nor for a friend.

SOCRATES: Then why do the young men go out to
be killed in war?

MARK TWAIN: The old bunk——

RABELAIS (*Aside*): *Qu'est-ce que c'est?* "Bunk."
Bunk.

VOLTAIRE (*Aside*): *Je ne sais pas.*

MARK TWAIN: Loyalty. Patriotism. Duty. The
flag—their country. Their country—Hell!

J. PIERPONT MORGAN: Isn't it their country?

MARK TWAIN: Bunk. Their country as much as
Louisiana was the country of the slaves on the sugar
plantations or South Carolina the country of the poor
brutes in the rice-swamps.

SOCRATES: To me it is not so simple. Do you not
believe pride moves men to foolish conduct of which
reason would disapprove?

INGERSOLL: Certainly.

SOCRATES: And public opinion is most powerful.

INGERSOLL: Certainly; most powerful.

SOCRATES: May not the very romance of war at-
tract young men who lead a monotonous, servile life?
Who may hope from war advancement they can never
hope for otherwise?

MARK TWAIN: Yes. But once get the young people, men and girls, to comprehend that war is *always* the struggle between the rulers of nations for control of lesser nations—for loot, gain, profits to the favored few, the master class, and you debunk the whole thing. Romance and all. What is there to be proud of? What romance is there in going out to die for a boss whose collar you wear? You are simply a fool. No pride in that. What's the glory in killing another poor fool like yourself? No pride in that; only shame.

VOLTAIRE: Bravo, Samuel.

MARK TWAIN: The flag follows the dollar.

MORGAN: And why not? International capitalists would never finance a foreign country or invest in foreign countries unless they were sure their investments would be protected by their own government.

LINCOLN: That means the boys of the plain people must be ordered out to die for your dollars?

MORGAN: No. They fight for their country.

LINCOLN: Their country—your dollars.

MORGAN: You cannot separate the capital of a country from the country any more than you can separate the mountains. If the investments of American capitalists were not secured by the army and navy, the capitalists would refuse to invest abroad. Collisions are inevitable. You cannot abolish war.

THOMAS JEFFERSON: An idea. Abolish the capitalists.

MORGAN: A dream. A fanatic's theory. There will always be capitalists. If they cannot find an outlet for their capital abroad, they will have to find investments at home, and that would play the devil. Interest would fall to nothing. It would be fierce, domestic competition and chaos.

THOMAS PAINE: An idea. Change the whole economic system. Abolish competition and war. No more money monarchs and—no more morons and slums—no more——

MORGAN: Do you want to Russianize a perfect country?

MARK TWAIN: What country?

MORGAN: The United States.

LINCOLN: Perfect?

INGERSOLL: Look down on earth. There is an example right now of how wars are hatched from foreign investments which are backed by the government—an example of how little the people or their boasted Congress have to do with making the wars they pay for and in which their sons die. One man may take a step —as Wilson did—and you are at war.

JESUS: What is this present example? I am not in the councils of the earth.

INGERSOLL: Some American capitalists got from a corrupt dictatorship of Mexico oil land concessions—and other land concessions.

GOD: Stop a moment, Robert. No government or power on earth has power to give away the earth from the people who inhabit it, use it, and need it.

INGERSOLL: Yes, but that is not law.

GOD: It is my law.

INGERSOLL: Man still gives land away by the old feudal paper title and the holder claims to own forever.

GOD: No one has any property right forever. Go on.

INGERSOLL: But by a revolution the people of Mexico claimed their own.

VOLTAIRE: Trouble.

INGERSOLL: And wrote a constitution declaring

among other things that the sub-soil (the things of value beneath the surface) could not be given away with the surface and all persons claiming such rights must apply to the government for a new lease—to ex-pire in fifty years.

MARK TWAIN:   Fair enough.

BEN FRANKLIN:   The oil will be gone in fifty years.

MORGAN:   It is confiscation.

INGERSOLL:   That's what the oil men say.

TOM PAINE:   It's Mexican soil, isn't it?

INGERSOLL:   Yes.

TOM PAINE:   The speculators got it from a Mexican government?

INGERSOLL:   Yes, from a dictator for his own profit.

JEFFERSON:   Fraud on the people.

TOM PAINE:   Can't Mexico make laws for its own soil? All Mexican landholders have to follow the new law, don't they?

INGERSOLL:   Yes.

TOM PAINE:   Why should Mexico's laws be enforced on Mexicans and set aside for stranger speculators?

MARK TWAIN:   Because the flag follows the dollar and the army and navy follow the flag.

MORGAN:   They ought to.   I tell you capitalists wouldn't do business without this insurance.

INGERSOLL:   Most of the foreign holders of oil concessions have applied for new fifty-year leases under the new constitution, but the really powerful ones—the Standard Oil—Sinclair and Doheny of Teapot Dome—refuse.

RABELAIS:   *Je ne comprend pas* "Doheny." "Doheny of Teapot Dome."

VOLTAIRE:   *Doheny est le Grand Seigneur de Teapot Dome et des Etats Unis.*

RABELAIS:   *Merci.*

INGERSOLL:   The Secretary of State of the United States backs up the oil speculators in refusing to obey Mexican laws on Mexican soil.

TOM PAINE:   Why?

MARK TWAIN:   Because Mexico is weak and the capitalists run the government.

MORGAN:   They ought to. Government after all is only business—and a big principle is at stake.

MARK TWAIN:   Big principal and big interest.

MORGAN:   I mean honor.

LINCOLN:   What?

MORGAN:   Honor.  Our national honor.

LINCOLN:   You mean investments.

MORGAN:   Same thing. We are in honor bound to protect our investors.

LINCOLN:   The slave power forced one war on Mexico.

JEFFERSON:   And this is another.

LINCOLN:   By the same power.  Property.

INGERSOLL:   Yes. There is the point. The Secretary of State encourages the oil speculators to resistance to Mexican laws.

MARK TWAIN:   Which all Mexicans must obey.

INGERSOLL:   He even says no matter what they do, he will protect, by war, if necessary, the interests of citizens of the United States.  He refuses arbitration and there you have a nice war egg laid by Nervous Nellie the Lame Duck, all by himself.

RABELAIS:   *Lem-dook—Lem-dook—Nellie la nerveuse.  Qu'est-ce que c'est?  "Lem-dook"?*

INGERSOLL:   A "lame duck" is a Congressman who has served his party better than he has served the people, and when the people spew him out and refuse to re-elect him, the party takes care of him as one wounded in its service. Otherwise, there would be no inducement for a Congressman to desert the people and take orders from the President.

VOLTAIRE: Do they pay in silver?

INGERSOLL: No. Not even thirty pieces.

MARK TWAIN: Though always the lame ducks have preferred to serve the Money Power.

INGERSOLL: They are given some office. In addition to a war egg in Mexico, the lame duck is laying another in Nicaragua, but it is really one nest.

RABELAIS: A lem-dook egg is lay in Nicaragua?

INGERSOLL: It is part of the same game. To control Mexico. There is a lawful president of Nicaragua, who is liberal and is supported by the people—Sacasa. There is a usurping president, supported by the State Department of the United States—Diaz.

LINCOLN: Why?

INGERSOLL: Because Nicaragua is weak. Were Nicaragua and Mexico strong Powers our conduct would be wholly different.

LINCOLN: It is bullying. It is infamous. It is cowardly. It will reap a harvest of hate.

JESUS: Is there never to be spirit, ideals? Always things, wealth, robbery? Never to do as you would be done by?

GAUTAMA: Always force—never discussion?

LINCOLN: What is the pretext for the United States meddling in the affairs of Nicaragua?

INGERSOLL: To protect American lives, property.

LINCOLN: Have any Americans been hurt?

INGERSOLL: None.

LINCOLN: Has any property been injured?

INGERSOLL: None.

LINCOLN: Now give the real reason for this new exhibition of the bullying imperialism of the United States.

INGERSOLL: The real reason is imperialism. Property-greed, lust of control, and fear or a pretense of fear that Russian communism is lodging in these now revolutionary countries. Diaz, dictator of Nicaragua, says to the Secretary of State of the United States: "Do as you like. All I ask is power, loot, and protection." Naturally the Secretary of State prefers a protectorate over Nicaragua and a president who is his own tool. It is a whip—no, a sword—against the people's rule in Mexico. So marines are rushed to Nicaragua to meddle in Nicaragua's internal affairs and suppress the lawful president and support the usurper. Three thousand marines are there already.

LINCOLN: I fear my country is on that common highway of nations which leads to wealth, power, imperialism, death.

VOLTAIRE: *Ah, ma belle France. Pardon!* Why will not Monsieur le lame duck Secretary arbitrate? Is not arbitration what the world now shouts for?

MARK TWAIN: With their mouths.

VOLTAIRE: Why will not the Honorable Lame Duck arbitrate?

INGERSOLL: He says there is only one side.

SOCRATES: But is the United States on one side?

INGERSOLL: Yes.

SOCRATES: And is Mexico on the other side?

INGERSOLL: Yes.

SOCRATES: Then even a sophist must admit there are two sides. Will the United States permit Mexico to decide?

INGERSOLL:   No.

SOCRATES:   Then it seems some impartial body must decide.

VOLTAIRE:   Seems rational.

MARK TWAIN:   That's the cripple's objection to it, perhaps.

RABELAIS:   Cripple?   Cripple?

MARK TWAIN:   The Lame Duck, the Secretary of State—a cripple.

RABELAIS:   *Ma fois*—"Run in"—"Cop"—"Lem—dook"—"Lem-dook egg"—"cripple"—*Quelle mélange!*

INGERSOLL:   Here you see two nice war eggs laid by one lame duck, and the people and their Congress will never be the wiser and will be helpless when they are hatched.

MARK TWAIN:   For the young men who are not killed it will be exciting.

TOM PAINE:   The people only fight and pay the cost.   The people always lose.

INGERSOLL:   A clash with the soldiers in Mexico; a clash with the marines in Nicaragua—war— and all for oil — for concessionaires, for "investors."   Nervous Nellie is only their valet and Congress helpless—except officially to declare war after a lame duck has made it.

GOD:   I am listening.   I am watching.   I will see the end.   It does occur to me in my infinite wisdom that if your common people were not common fools they would say, "Let those who go into foreign countries with their money take the risk of their investments or keep out.   We refuse to die for anybody's money."   What were you about to say, Abraham?

LINCOLN:   My country is sowing to the wind and will reap the whirlwind.   Hate, hate for the Ameri-

cans throughout all Latin countries.    All disputes can
be settled by discussion and arbitration between willing
countries, all but one.

VOLTAIRE:    What is that, Liberator?

LINCOLN:    Greed—the determination to seize, to
despoil.    A wolf will not arbitrate.

VOLTAIRE:    Why will not the Lame Duck arbitrate
with Mexico in friendly fashion?

INGERSOLL:    Because he is sure he is right.

RABELAIS:    *A bas le lem-dook.*

MARK TWAIN:    Reminds me of the Tlinkit Indians.
A friend of mine who was among them as a young man
told me they cremated their dead on great funeral
pyres, but the medicine men or priests they buried on
some promontory with a canoe turned over the grave
and a flagpole and flag to mark it, so the Great Spirit
would not carelessly overlook his priest.    My friend
asked an old Indian why the Shamans were not burned.
"Because they will not burn" was the answer.    "But,"
persisted my friend, who was of a non-theological,
doubting mind himself, "why don't you try?"    The
old man looked at him awhile as impassive as a stone
image, then said, with conclusive contempt: "What
would be the use of *trying* when we already know they
won't burn."    I think that is Nervous Nellie's state of
mind on arbitrating with Mexico.    Why try?    He
knows he is right.

LINCOLN:    Or knowing he is wrong, fears the light.

JESUS:    Those who intend evil love darkness.

GOD:    The United States is at the very pinnacle of
wealth and power and this will last a long time, but
even now it is headed toward destruction.    Greed be-
gets hate and hate devours.

JESUS:    The only life is love.

(God *is standing on the Parapet of Heaven, listening to* Lao-tze, Gautama, *and* Jesus *conversing.*)

Jesus:   I don't see why it should be difficult to distinguish between what destroys and what constructs.

Gautama:   Because hate that destroys is natural to man.   Hunger, fear, and hate are his primal emotions.

Lao-tze:   Hate and fear are the black principles of ignorance and belong to the brutes.   Love and trust are of the white principles of spirit.   To reach them one must have wings.

Gautama:   The wings of thought; only by spiritual contemplation can we reach to the higher things which are not of the body.

Jesus:   Not of the earth, earthy.   Ah, that is it. Of the earth, earthy; material—heavy—weighing down. Things, things, things.

Lao-tze:   Power.   Power.   Power.

Gautama:   Possessions—not thoughts.

Lao-tze:   Who is richer, he who is loaded with land and gold, with power over many, or he who by thought possesses the universe and by love draws all to him?

Jesus:   It is so clear to us.   Why not to man, to whom the All-Father gave the germ of reason, the seed of love?   One day on earth, during the Great War,

I heard one young man say he would refuse to kill his brethren. He knew no cause that would justify the slaughter of men, women, and children; least of all a cause which was no other than a contest for the possession of the planet as wolves contend for a carcass. Then those around him said: "So you are one of those damned fools who believe in Jesus—we will show you where Jesus is." They reviled him, knocked him down, and killed him. Must my name cause murder?

LAO-TZE: Neither your name nor your teaching, my brother, but the jungle rage that still abides with men.

JESUS: But I thought to conquer that jungle rage by love.

MARK TWAIN: Miserably ignorant and full of hate and fear as the herd is, yet you have not died in vain. I myself have seen your fruit. Badger Flat—a placer mining camp—was a horde of all manner of men—all colors—all nations; adventurers, pirates, brigands, scholars, poets, scientists, men of every trade and business, and of no trade or business. Each one, because of distrust, carried his gun at his belt, his knife in his boot. The saloons were countless, the churches none. The click of the roulette wheel and the shuffle of the faro deck were constant. And not a week passed but one or more bodies lay on the billiard table or the bar, covered with a sheet of canvas, waiting burial.

The cemetery on the hill grew faster than anything else in the camp, but there were few headboards and each one might have carried, "He was not quick enough on the trigger." That was the whole morals of the camp—Shoot first. Of course, mistakes were made, but apologies were useless. Every man was a good shot.  You had to be.  No one left any home address, so if a mistake was made it was just buried and forgotten—bygones were bygones.

One day a red-headed fellow, with a beard that was golden in the sun, tramped into camp, his outfit on his back.  He had neither horse nor mule—not even a burro.

He smiled at everybody, asked "The Pig under the Gate" if he could cut wood or do any jobs for his meals and began to enquire around about claims.  Everything was staked out, or had been; except the burial ground, and that was too high for water.  So after looking around a day or two, he picked out a spot no one had located—at least it had only been scratched and abandoned.

The stranger had a pick and shovel—and boots; he fixed up a cradle and went to work.  There was plenty of water for his claim, I will say that.  Well, this idiot —excuse me—this follower of yours——

JESUS:  I understand.

MARK TWAIN:  This red-headed fellow carried no gun and no knife except a jack-knife to whittle with. Presently he began preaching the foolishness of murder and the true wisdom of the Golden Rule, if you would only trust it.  He said the trouble with men was fear. If you didn't make people afraid of you, you needn't be afraid of them.  If you didn't want to hog what didn't belong to you but were willing to do as you would be done by, there was no need of guns and knives.

Of course, everyone said he was a fool, and all thought he was off his head, but he talked well and had a lot to tell the miners, saloonkeepers, and camp-women—that's all there was to the camp—that was mighty interesting and he could recite poetry. Still, all agreed he must be crazy. One thing did pan out as he said it would. No one was afraid of him. No one was on guard against him and they would as soon have thought of drawing on a baby as on the Rule. Someone began calling him "Golden Rule"—then it got to be "Golden," but that became mixed up with his beard instead of his notions, so they called him "the Rule" and finally just "Rule."

Things went on as before for a while; lead was settling disputes and men falling all 'round, but Rule was just as calm as a girl picking blackberries. He never dodged nor got out of the way and would go over to help the one that dropped, but of course that was useless; these men weren't amateurs. All the time Rule was preaching his gospel.

Little by little, you could hardly say how, the shooting began to drop off a bit. The men were more trustful. Finally most of the shooting was between drunks. This discouraged hard drinking. A camp court was set up to settle disputes.

Rule worked his claim but nothing doing. He had to do jobs for his grub part of the time. He was awfully friendly with the camp-women; made medicine tea for them from bark or leaves or roots, and tended "Magpie Mag" when she had small-pox and was put away by herself in a cabin, out of camp. "It's what I'd want her to do for me," he said.

One day Rule walked into the Nugget and laid on the bar one of its namesakes, weighing fifteen ounces. In a few days another weighing seven ounces—and then the prize nugget, thirty-eight ounces.

It looked as if all the gold of the mountains was in

Rule's claim. His bedrock was just loaded with little common stuff like beans. The camp was wild. Everything around Rule was staked and re-staked, but there wasn't any shooting. Didn't seem right in his vicinity —and with the camp court ready to do business.

But in every jungle there is always a tiger that knows no law but tooth and claw—and one day it was noticed that Cut-throat Samson was working Rule's claim. He got his name from a scar on his throat, but he was well named anyway. He had killed two men in this camp and God knows—Excuse me.

GOD: That's all right, Samuel. I am interested.

MARK TWAIN: And he must have left a lot more on his trail.

Rule was found packing up to leave. He had expressed out his nuggets and dust and was just packing his kit and a book or two, smiling, and not saying anything, but there was a wildfire of curiosity in the camp.

So it came out that Cut-throat had ordered him out of his claim and out of camp. Rule said, "Now men, no trouble. You think I'm a coward, but it's my rule and I'll live and die by it."

That evening Cut-throat's body was swinging from a pine with a notice stuck in it with a knife, "Take Notice. This camp is run by the Golden Rule." I call that living up to your spirit, Jesus.

JESUS: Not exactly. Resist not evil with evil.

MARK TWAIN: That's what Rule said. He wouldn't stay. I never heard of him again.

GOD: He is here.

MARK TWAIN: Here?

GOD: Come with me—we will all visit him.

MARK TWAIN:   Well, this is a pleasure I did not expect even in heaven.   Rule here.   The Golden Rule here.   This beats the devil.

JESUS:   It will.

(*All go out.*)

## XXXIX
### Satan Asks for Help

(God *is standing beneath a heavenly arch holding a* *world in each hand, His arms outspread.* Hermes *comes in.*)

Hermes:   Supreme Majesty, Satan desires audience.

God:   He is very welcome. Bring him here at once. (*Hermes goes out.*)   I have learned that even I can change and grow.   I used to regard Satan as the enemy of the universe.   Now I see it was only difference of view.   He also must have his freedom.   We balance each other as I these spheres.

(Satan *and* Hermes *come in.*)
You are welcome.   I am sincerely glad to see you.   In fact, I have missed you.   We seem necessary to each other.

Satan:   I always thought so.   May I ask what you are doing?

God:   I am testing these two dead worlds.

Satan:   Do you intend to renew their life?

God:   O, no.   I never do that.   The dead is forever dead in its old form.   That is the salvation of the universe.   I intend to use them as life in another form. See.   Now they are a single orb full of light and life. It begins its flight.

SATAN:  Which ephemeral man calls endless.

GOD:  Nothing is endless.  Well, what now?  Let us repose.

(*They lie down together on a bank overlooking space.*)

SATAN:  I am in a little trouble and you can help me.

GOD:  I?

SATAN:  Yes.  Quite consistently with your new ideas that we are not so far apart.

GOD:  Well?

SATAN:  I am from Washington.  Washington, D. C., Earth.

GOD:  You still dwell on the earth?

SATAN:  It is my only home now.  But it engages my entire time.  After the war to end war I thought my occupation would be gone.  But I am busier than ever.  The war was like a ferment—a most astounding lot of results are buzzing around me like flies— new wars—and preparations for wars—greater speed than ever.  My particular home, the United States, is swollen with imperialism, conquest, and lust for material things—it alone is enough to keep me busy.  Injustice, ambition, deceit, diplomacy, conquest—all the old evils overgrown and with new families—the head of the United States is a man so wooden they call him Dumb Cal.  The Big Financial Interests just play with him.  You know they and I are one.  We are swelling like dried apples in water.  Everything is going all right.  Nervous Nellie has the U. S. on the edge of war with Mexico; has swallowed Nicaragua and incurred the deep-seated hate of all the Latin countries in South America, perhaps in the world.  You know what hate means in my business?

SATAN CONVERSES WITH GOD

God: I didn't understand the name of your new associate.

Satan: Nervous Nellie. That's just a *nom de guerre*. His name is Kellogg. He is Secretary of State.

God: Why Nervous Nellie?

Satan: Excuse me. Here are some of our old friends.

(Voltaire, Rabelais, Mark Twain, Robert Ingersoll, Tom Paine, Mary Wollstonecraft, Margaret Fuller, Carrie Nation, Lenin, *and others come in.*)

I am glad to see you all again.

All but Carrie Nation: We are glad to see you.

Carrie Nation: I am not.

Satan: You think not—but you really are. What would you do without me?

God: Our friend here——

Carrie Nation: Friend! I simply can't understand, God.

God: Our friend was telling me some earth news and of a friend of his called Nervous Nellie.

Ingersoll: O, Kellogg, Secretary of State of the United States.

Satan: Yes. Yes. The All-Knowing One was just asking me why he is called Nervous Nellie.

Lenin: I can tell you—he sees my ghost everywhere.

Satan: Yes, yours and a perfect host of others—all Russian.

Lenin: Does he really see them or does he pretend for a purpose?

Satan: O, he really sees them. I have possessed him so he sees hosts of Bolshevik devils everywhere.

Mark Twain: Reminds me of a darkey roustabout

on the Mississippi. He saw the devil every time he
turned around in the dark. One evening he saw some
flood drift hanging on a stake and it waved to him—
that was the devil sure—so he ran like a scared jack-
rabbit till he saw a tall stump with a knot-hole through
which the sky shone. That was the devil's eye and he
ran till he came to a belted Holstein cow. Her head
and middle were white. All the rest of her was black
and invisible. Our colored friend saw a head with
horns, separate from the body and the body moving
through the air without legs. With one yell he jumped
into the river and it took a quart of whiskey to get the
devil out of him. That's Nervous Nellie and Bolshevism.

LENIN: We might send the hysterical one some
vodka.

INGERSOLL: He needs more than vodka.

LINCOLN: Common sense, perhaps. Is the United
States so weak it must fear a new idea?

VOLTAIRE: All "statesmen" do.

MORGAN: You Bolsheviks deceive yourselves. He
has more sense than all of you. Besides, he is acting
under orders.

INGERSOLL: Whose orders?

MORGAN: The President's.

MARK TWAIN: Dumb Cal. And whose orders is
he obeying?

MORGAN: Silent Calvin. He senses our wishes.
Silence is golden.

MARK TWAIN: You bet it is. The silence of gold.

MORGAN: Why shouldn't the President carry out
the wishes of capital? Doesn't capital make the country?

LENIN: The capitalists are "The People."

MORGAN: Certainly they are. I am glad you see that now. Your former country has been forced to adopt the capitalistic system, but it has not given up its crazy socialistic ideas and is trying to promote revolution everywhere. The Secretary of State, whom you deride as Nervous Nellie, knows that Russia is back of all trouble in Mexico and Nicaragua. Russia is back of this confiscation of land.

INGERSOLL: Confiscation hell. It offers fifty-year leases free. The new constitution was passed twelve years ago.

MORGAN: I don't care if it was. It is only being put into effect now that a progressive Russianized administration has come into power, and Secretary Kellogg knows it.

LENIN: He was asked for a show-down and could show nothing.

MORGAN: Didn't Mr. Olds, Assistant Secretary of State, show it?

LENIN: Mr. Olds told the newspaper men a lot of romance for which he admitted he had no proof—and when the newspaper men said they could not spread such news over the country without some assurance of its truth, he said he was morally certain Russia was at work in Mexico and begged them to inflame the country with this lie, though he knew at the time that the President of Mexico had proclaimed that no propaganda of Russia would be permitted. The newspaper men at the capital believe that Mr. Olds is either too dishonest or too credulous for his position. He is certainly too dangerous.

VOLTAIRE: *Mais non*. Falsification is the soul of diplomacy, but if he failed to put over a falsehood, then certainly he is not fit for his position.

MORGAN: Anyway, Mr. Kellogg knows Russia is raising the devil all over the world.

SATAN: Did some one speak to me?

GOD: No. Only took your name in vain.

SATAN: Many do. And yours.

GOD: Yes. They confuse us.

SATAN: What was said of me?

GOD: Pierpont said you were a Bolshevik.

SATAN: He flatters me. In the French Revolution the kings called me a Republican. I am many-in-one.

MORGAN: Why shouldn't we——

GOD: We?

MORGAN: It's a habit. Why shouldn't the United States by armed forces establish a protectorate over Nicaragua and Mexico? It is self-defense. Revolution might spread from them to us—to the United States.

TOM PAINE: And since when has the United States been so afraid of revolution? Revolutions are the bursting of swaddling clothes.

JEFFERSON: Where would the world be without its revolutionists? English, American, French, Italian, and Russian.

LENIN: The Soviets are not the whole Russian Revolution. Only one little bud. But we desire to flower and fruit. It is early to judge; the Russian Revolution will surely live, no matter what becomes of the Soviets.

MORGAN: You deny free speech and press to whatever attacks the government, attacks your infamous system.

LENIN: So does the United States.

MORGAN: Our press and speech are perfectly free unless they attack our government, our system.

LENIN:   So is ours.

MORGAN:   But your system is infamous.

LENIN:   We think yours is.

MORGAN:   Ha! That's just it. He admits it. He would like to change the system we have found so satisfactory. Russia ought to be suppressed everywhere.

MARK TWAIN:   Be calm. The sons and daughters of the American Revolution will stop any revolution.

TOM PAINE:   Shades of the Fathers. What descendants.

JEFFERSON:   A free country moving toward justice need not fear revolution.

TOM PAINE:   Ah, justice.

LINCOLN:   You cannot breed revolution in a country where the people are contented and their souls feel justice is with them, but if a people is ripe for revolution you cannot stop it.

SOCRATES:   Not hardships make revolution, but injustice.

TOM PAINE:   Economic inequality. There must be freedom. All theories must be discussed and tried—there is no possible test of political systems but trial.

LINCOLN:   With such freedom change is pleasant and easy—no need for revolution. It is growth.

SOCRATES:   The rulers must be just men.

CONFUCIUS:   With no thought to do to others except as they would wish others to do to them.

GAUTAMA:   The root of all is soul—not things.

JESUS:   The only power—love.

LENIN:   Russia believes she is loving humanity.

MORGAN:   You repudiate your international debts. Do you call that loving humanity?

LENIN:   Perhaps. They were loaded on to wretched slaves by an autocrat.

MORGAN: That makes no difference. That idea would repudiate all debts.

LENIN: Russia has offered to meet your country around the table for a discussion and an accounting. We have claims also.

MORGAN: For what?

LENIN: For damages inflicted by the United States in arming and financing counter-revolutions and invasions—for a blockade that denied even anaesthetics to the suffering.

MORGAN: Those are not debts.

INGERSOLL: Wait. Wait. The United States claimed damages against Great Britain for permitting the Confederate cruiser Alabama to be fitted out in a British port.

LINCOLN: And was allowed the claim, and the damages were paid.

INGERSOLL: It was settled around a table by a commission.

LENIN: As Russia now proposes.

MORGAN: That's different. We don't recognize Russia.

LINCOLN: Why not?

MORGAN: Because she repudiates her debt to us.

LINCOLN: And refuse to meet her in discussion because she is not recognized. A snake with his tail in his mouth.

VOLTAIRE: And my country, *la belle France?* Has she paid her debts?

INGERSOLL: No, and says she never will.

MORGAN: Says she can't—that's different.

INGERSOLL: "Can't" is a matter of opinion. She is expanding army and navy—waging war in Africa—war of conquest—and she refuses to even meet in con-

ference to discuss cutting down the naval forces of
the world.

VOLTAIRE: *Ah, la patrie. Toujours l'empire.*

RABELAIS: *Toujours la gloire.* I remember once
when I was with Cardinal Bellay at court——

VOLTAIRE: *Un moment, mon ami, s'il vous plait.*
France says she owes but will not pay. Russia says
she does not owe but will pay on an accounting?

LENIN: Yes.

VOLTAIRE: *Parbleu.* I prefer Russia.

RABELAIS: *Nom de Dieu. Moi aussi.*

VOLTAIRE: *Excusez, compatriot. Vous?*

RABELAIS: *N'importe.* I was only going to say the
king levied a tax to make war.

TOM PAINE: All taxes are to make war. The others
are nothing.

RABELAIS: Then through the years more wars;
more taxes; *enfin,* no king. They cut off his head.

VOLTAIRE: Repudiation?

RABELAIS: *Oui.*

MORGAN: We have no kings.

VOLTAIRE: No heads to cut off. O, *monsieur,* you
have purse-strings, privileges, monopolies, money-sacks.
Eh? These can be guillotined also. A little too obstinate on these—and—hm—revolution? Eh, *monsieur?*

MORGAN: The government—the army—the navy—
the police are ours. They will protect us and our property.

VOLTAIRE: But so—*Eh bien. N'importe.* We are
in heaven.

RABELAIS: *Hélas.*

GOD: Why do you sigh, François?

RABELAIS: Memories, Omniscience, memories.

VOLTAIRE: Tell us a story, *mon ami.*

RABELAIS: *Mais non. J'ai soif.*

VOLTAIRE: *Impossible.* You are dead, you are in heaven.

RABELAIS: *Hélas.* That is why I am *triste*—sad—I shall be thirsty—through eternity.

VOLTAIRE: Forget it.

RABELAIS: I can't.

VOLTAIRE: Tell us a story.

RABELAIS: There was a lean pig which roamed the lanes seeking industriously wherewith to live. One day a man put him in a pen and brought him carrots and turnips and barley and wheat and cabbage stalks and leaves and many succulent things. The pig laughed and grew fat. He stretched himself on his straw and grunted: See how this man serves me; he is my slave. One day there was much fire under a caldron, and great steam from it. The pig said, "My slave prepares for me a fine new dish." But soon he was in the caldron himself, and presently he was hanging in the kitchen as hams and sausages.

VOLTAIRE: *Toujours les saucissons. Toujours.*

RABELAIS: It was a revolution.

MARK TWAIN: O Master. That is a moral not a story. Tell us a story.

GOD: Do, François.

RABELAIS: A certain beautiful young nun and a certain beautiful young priest—I knew him well—met so often in confessional that they learned to love each other.

GOD: They do not learn that, François.

RABELAIS: *Pardon. Non.* They loved each other. You know Lord—it does happen.

GOD: Surely I know. The dear things. Go on.

RABELAIS: They loved each other so, the very souls

of them came out of the body and united as one. But there were the rules of the church and the rules of the order. Even to love was wicked.

GOD: With the church, François,—with the church.

RABELAIS: Yes. Yes—with the church.

GOD: The church is man.

RABELAIS: Yes, the church is man. Never could they be alone except in the confessional stall—and you know yourself, Lord, that the confessional stall with only a little whispering hole is not a place for lovers. They were not happy there.

GOD: I do not order it so, François.

RABELAIS: Never could they meet freely. You know, Lord, how lovers long to be free; no ears but the leaves, no eyes but the stars—you understand.

GOD: I understand, François.

RABELAIS: They were young. Only these two against the great church; against the whole mass of the people. Two young white doves driven out to sea by a furious storm. No hope in the seething waters below—they were not brave to drown. They caught at a dead stick; deceit and lies. They cloaked their love from all sight. The young priest would take solitary walks from his monastery to the seashore—to a point opposite her convent. There in the dusk of evenings he built a shelter; a rough poor shelter of the stones and boulders worn by the ages. It looked like part of the shore. No one noticed it, but it would keep out the wind and weather, and the floor was clean, soft, white sand. Now the poor child in the convent could not keep her secret. It grew in her as by a mountain rill in the spring a green sword pricks up which grows till it bursts all bonds and flings a cluster of asphodels against the sun. With tears and sobs she told her wickedness to the one who seemed to invite it: a nun with saintly face, recently come to the convent. This Mother in God smoothed the girl's hair and kissed her and said it was not the devil's work; for God, and God only, had created love; God and God only had sent love into our poor empty bosoms. The young nun and the elder one walked every evening to the seashore to the stone oratory the young monk had builded. There, in one sunset, the splendor of which outshone all splendor, the young woman met the young man. The lovers forgot the guardian, forgot everything but love. When they came to themselves Sister Cecilia was nowhere to be seen, but when the lovers were ready to separate— no; lovers are never ready to separate; but when they must return to their separate cells, Sister Cecilia joined them—out of the air, it seemed. Daily, or as near as might be, the elder and the younger nun would walk to the sea, and the elder, pausing some distance away, would kiss her sister and motion her to go on to her joy. There she would meet her lover and in the rude cell he had constructed they would worship God; the mighty sea thundering an eternal high mass for them; not more eternal than love. The celebration of creation.

One morning, as the sun was rising, there was a feeble wail in the cell of the young nun. Yes, that small weak cry of humanity to the world. Sister Cecilia was there. She kissed the wet brow of the young mother and smoothed the damp hair. She murmured "Blessed art thou above women. Peace, peace." She called the abbess—and said "Blessed is this house and all who are of it. The Lord has descended. Here too is a son of God, born of a virgin". The abbess fell on her knees, and prayed, and thanked God. The great news was sent to the Abbey; but the abbot was a world-

ly man (else he had not been abbot).   He was a skep-
tic.   He ordered an inquisition.   Even as he did so he
was told there was a nun at the gate asking for him.
He went down to the gate and beheld Sister Cecilia.
When the abbot saw her, he knew he was in the pres-
ence of a heavenly one.   He bowed before her.

"Listen to the command of God," she said.   "A son
has been born to a virgin; and God has taken the mother
to his bosom.   She is dead.   The son is of the church
but not for the church.   See that he be brought up as
a son of God."   Even as she spoke she vanished; vanished before his very eyes and he knew an angel had
visited him; an angel sent to earth to do the will of
God.

The young priest was smitten as an oak is smitten
by lightning, but he became the most pious abbot of
his monastery; pious for the brotherhood of men not
for the power of the church.   When he was abbot he
caused a chapel to be built in honor of the Virgin
Mother, and her body was carried there with great
ceremony and he himself said solemn high mass over it.
He kept a place beside her for himself; where in God's
time he was laid in eternal rest.   Now in after ages
there stood in this place amid the ruins of the chapel
three beautiful bay trees whose fragrant limbs inter-
twined.

SATAN:  Three?

RABELAIS:   Yes, the son became great in the councils
of men—teaching brotherhood and peace—but he dis-
appeared.   A long time after, an old man came from
India, so full of love and wisdom and the gentle spirit
of God that he was reverenced by the monastery, the
convent, and the people; but he would not enter the
monastery even as a lay brother; when he lay dying he

asked that his body also be placed in the chapel—by the side of the other two.  This was done—the people weeping.  I hope I have not offended, Omniscient and All-Forgiving.

GOD:  We thank you, François.

SATAN:  It seems sacrilege, but may I recall your attention to my own trouble?

GOD:  Certainly, shall my all-hearing ear be open to men and denied to you?  What is it?

SATAN:  It's this Washington business.

GOD:  George?  George Washington?

SATAN:  No—D. C.—District of Columbia.

GOD:  O I don't care where it is.  How does it interest you?

SATAN:  It's my headquarters.

GOD:  Yes.

SATAN:  Now Nervous Nellie——

GOD:  True—We'd forgotten her—Is it he or she?

SATAN:  Both.  He wears pants but is as timid as skirts.

GOD:  I thought you had afflicted him.

SATAN:  So I have.  That's all right.

INGERSOLL:  Seems to me they need Joshua Higgins in the U. S. State Department.

MARK TWAIN:  Tell us——

INGERSOLL:  O, he was a dried-up old Yankee who boated people about during the summer at the Isle of Shoals.  He was so careful he was the favorite boatman with the ladies.  One day he was rowing a lady about and, just to show her sympathy, she said:

"Mr. Higgins, what do you do for a living through the winter?"  "Waal," said he, with that nasal drawl, "I'm putty thrifty and put by a good bit durin' the summer, and in winter I make abeout a dollar and a half a week sleepin' 'reound with timid wimmin."

MARK TWAIN: Sure, he belongs with Nervous Nellie.

INGERSOLL: And he'd be welcome at the White House.

GOD: Is Nervous Nellie your trouble?

SATAN: No, O, no. I'm depending on him to start the next war. It won't be much of a war; but still in these days you have to take what you can get. Of course Mexico, Nicaragua, or even China can't fight the United States just now, but it's the future I'm looking to. I am depending on Nervous Nellie to make the United States the best-hated country on earth. You know what a power hate is.

JESUS: For destruction.

SATAN: Yes—that's my job. Yours is upbuilding.

JESUS: By love.

SATAN: Don't think, brother——

CARRIE NATION: Brother! Jesus, hit him.

JESUS: Be quiet, Carrie; resist not evil.

CARRIE NATION: O, I wish I had my hatchet.

JESUS: Quiet, Carrie. Force gets you nowhere. Try to learn that.

SATAN: I was going to say, don't think I am as stupid as mankind. I know love is not weak sentimentality but is the strongest force in the universe, I know if man ever believes this—O, I don't mean with his silly mouth—he does that now—Sundays—I mean if he ever truly understands the power of your teaching as he understands business and war and believes in love as a force just as he believes in dynamite and money now, I am beaten. You have the best of it, as a cosmic principle, but I have the best of it in the stupidity of man. That's our game. You teach love and I teach hate. Up to date I have won. I have the weaker principle but man believes in mine, heart and soul.

JESUS: You know hate and force are weaker than love.

SATAN: I know it but man doesn't. He trusts hate. He doesn't trust love, and as hate is destructive I will win. Man will destroy himself.

JESUS: I yet have a million years to try to make him understand.

SATAN: Take two million; I will win.

JESUS: Father—Father.

GOD: It is as Satan has said. Man must save himself. I gave him reason—he has not developed it.

SATAN: I am sorry for you, brother. The game is fair. You for love, I for hate.

GOD: But what is your trouble?

SATAN: I have a man in charge of prohibition in the United States, Wayne B. Wheeler.

GOD: Where is he?

SATAN: O, in Washington. All the monkey business is in Washington.

RABELAIS: Monkey—Monkey—Funny-mentalist?

SATAN: Not now, please. *Excusez*. I put Wayne B. Wheeler in charge of prohibition which if properly handled would have been of great help to me. Intolerance—hate again—hate among Christians—I'm sorry, Jesus.

GOD: But this prohibition. I prohibit nothing. You cannot grow by prohibitions.

SATAN: I know. I know. It is contrary to you and that's why it is so good for me. It all depends on man's stupidity. Intolerance or prohibition this time is against alcoholic liquors—wine—beer.

SOCRATES:  The Egyptians drank beer.  Everybody drank wine.

SATAN:  And spirits.

GOD:  Angels?

SATAN:  No—whiskey—brandy—alcoholic spirits. Well, all I wanted was intolerance and hate—but this Wheeler has bungled the whole thing.  He is so vulgar, intemperate, and abusive that he disgusts people. Such a fanatic that he makes intolerance hateful.  I want it to look right.  The other day the president of Columbia College—one of man's institutions of learning, so-called—this President Butler gave a talk against this liquor prohibition and was clever enough to point out that a far more important thing than liquor was involved.  That is personal liberty, the right of peaceable men to live their own lives; also that a very important spiritual asset was involved—tolerance.  He showed that prohibition was the very height of intolerance.

Now if Wheeler had been fit for my job, he never would have noticed truths he can't answer.  Every time he breaks loose I lose ground.  This time he said President Butler had a yellow streak in him—was the friend of bootleggers—speak-easies—drunkards—prostitutes; called him a "Personal Liberty" fanatic——

GOD:  Well I'm a little touched that way myself.

SATAN:  Of course; that was our first difference.

GOD:  And you were right.

SATAN:  Thanks.  Well, Wheeler's vulgar abuse was not argument.  It was just vulgar abuse, and he said he never would permit Butler to be President of the United States.  Butler has political ambitions.

INGERSOLL:  Can Wheeler say who is to be President?

SATAN: Well, I had it nearly in my hands. No judge could be appointed and pretty much no one elected to office without my permission as head of the prohibitionists. Yes, Wheeler does dictate judicial appointments, or did.

GOD: I wouldn't think people so non-understanding of my own principles of freedom could be powerful.

SATAN: They are not in fact—they are a minority, but they make up in fanaticism and noise.

MARK TWAIN: Like the one frog in the puddle.

SATAN: Wheeler is simply loading me down with drunkards—boys and girls. I don't want drunkards. They are refuse—garbage—a handicap.

GOD: But I thought he was against drinking.

SATAN: He is—he won't eat mince-pie.

GOD: Drink it, you mean.

SATAN: No—it's a pie.

GOD: I don't know anything about it. Go on.

SATAN: He is opposed to drinking, so he has taken the taste and aroma out of beer. He forbids everything—everything. The sick can't get good brandy or wine. Everything with over the half of one per cent of alcohol is prohibited. You remember how it was with Eve and that apple tree?

GOD: Yes. Another one of my mistakes. I have learned the prohibitions must come from within by the growth of the soul.

JESUS: Force never did anything but put back growth.

SATAN: Yes, but I don't want men to learn that. If they did, you might win.

GOD: But your trouble?

SATAN: He drives people to dives, cellars, and humiliating dens for just a decent glass such as always used to be a harmless friendly act.  Now it is a crime.  He has the United States act as murderer and put poison in the alcohol it releases for industrial use, and when poor ignorant laborers die of the poison he applauds and says "serves 'em right—another drunkard gone."

GOD:  What sort of people are they to endure this?

SATAN:  They won't.  They won't forever, and don't you see where it is hurting me?  I wanted intolerance and hate to spread.  Now intolerance and hate are all on the prohibition side and he is simply loading me up with young drunkards and criminals.  The schoolboys and girls carry their own saloons in their pockets.

GOD:  Why don't you get rid of him?

SATAN:  Ah—there is my trouble.  I can't.  That's what I have come to you for.

GOD:  Can't get rid of your own agent?

SATAN:  No, I can't, without shattering my own machine.

GOD:  What can I do?

SATAN:  Drive him crazy.

GOD:  Why, I can't make him any more crazy than he is.  Besides, I am opposed to special interventions.

SATAN:  This is important.

GOD:  No—not for anything.  I might advise him to quit.

SATAN:  He wouldn't.  He thinks he is you.

GOD:  O then let him alone.  Those people always come to an early end.  At least some day he will die, and prove once more my wisdom of death.

SATAN:  But think of me, meantime—Nervous Nellie doing fine on his side.  War and hate and this fellow loading me up with young drunkards.  Criminals and such trash.

GOD: Sorry, but I can not help you.

SATAN: Well, I still can depend on man's stupidity —but I am disappointed.

GOD: Sorry.

SATAN: I must be getting back to Washington. I don't know what may have happened. Goodbye.

JESUS: I am troubled about those young boy and girl drunkards. Couldn't you put a little more love into your friend's heart?

SATAN: Not the half of one per cent. You don't know a prohibitionist. What he professes to love is mankind. What he really loves is himself and his opinions. Goodbye.

ALL: Goodbye.

(SATAN *goes out.*)

GOD: A clever fellow. He has the winning side, my son. Hate and ignorance.

JESUS: The million years, Father, the million years.

## XL

### NOAH'S CRUISE

(GOD *is on the veranda of one of his heavenly mansions, playing chess with* BUDDHA. DARWIN, INGERSOLL, TOM PAINE, MARK TWAIN, RABELAIS, VOLTAIRE, CARRIE NATION, MADAME CURIE, *and others come in, talking.*)

INGERSOLL: Darwin, doesn't this Scopes trial down on earth make you laugh?

DARWIN: No, Robert. Ignorance is never amusing to me.

MME. CURIE: Nor to me. It is sad.

TOM PAINE: The fetter of mankind.

INGERSOLL: Well, to me it is comic.

MARK: Fools are always comic.

RABELAIS: What is it? This Scopes trial? For heresy? Eh? Another burning?

INGERSOLL: Yes, for heresy. Scopes believes in science.

RABELAIS: Does he attack the holy dogmas of our blessed church?

INGERSOLL: No, no. Only the myths of the Bible.

RABELAIS: Patience. He will yet be sainted.

VOLTAIRE: But what is it? The trial?

INGERSOLL: The State of Tennessee has a law making it a crime to teach that man is descended from any of the lower animals.

MME. CURIE: *Ma foi.* Stupid.

PAINE: Laws. Laws. Laws. Is it not strange that a minority of ignorant fanatics can make a whole state, a whole nation ridiculous?

INGERSOLL: Prohibition, for example.

PAINE: O, every interference by the state with the lives and thoughts of peaceable individuals. When will men learn that progress is hitched to freedom's chariot? The right of the obscene to be obscene, the wicked to be wicked, just as important as the right of the pure to be pure, the good to be good—otherwise there is no freedom. Progress is by education and evolution in absolute freedom. Every act of force is an obstruction.

DARWIN: But why this law? No one believes that man is descended from one of the lower animals. That is not evolution.

CARRIE NATION: What is evolution, atheist?

PAINE: Sounds familiar.

VOLTAIRE: *Moi aussi.*

DARWIN: Evolution is the simple general principle that in the countless ages life has existed on the planet, man and all other forms of life, animal and vegetable, have evolved from earlier lower forms; each in its own environment and its own line of development.

CARRIE NATION: Didn't you deny that God made man of clay, in his own image, and breathed the breath of life into him?

MARK TWAIN: Must have been rubber, not clay.

CARRIE NATION: And then made Eve of one of his ribs?

VOLTAIRE: How beautiful is faith.

RABELAIS: Ah, *mon ami.* I was in my time something of a physician. How well I remember my admiration of the skill of *le bon Dieu* who assembled so quickly the difficult machine: bones, muscles, nerves, heart, lungs, bowels, sight, hearing, taste, touch, smell; and the mysterious glands, all at once in working order, in a moment, from clay, and then,—*parbleu!*—not to repeat the task, he extracts from a rib that delightful Eve, with just the necessary agreeable changes so she may become the mother of the race.

VOLTAIRE: Hush! God is laughing—he hears you.

GOD: I hear all things. Check, Gautama.

(ST. PETER *comes in.*)

ST. PETER: Lord, a soul has just arrived from earth and wishes to see you. He says it is important.

GOD: Certainly.

(ST. PETER *goes out and brings in the soul of* WILLIAM JENNINGS BRYAN.)

ST. PETER: God, this is William Jennings Bryan—Earth.

BRYAN: You may say I have not run the race, you may say I have not fought the fight, but you cannot say I have not kept the faith.

GOD: As you saw it, William, as you saw it—but can you endure difference of thought? This is the place of infinite tolerance. That is why it is heaven.

BRYAN: I cannot be tolerant with those who press down on the brow of labor a crown of thorns and crucify it on a cross of gold. I cannot be tolerant to those who attack our religion and our Bible, your sacred word.

(JESUS *comes in.*)

I cannot be tolerant to the wine sellers.

GOD: Get over the idea that the Hebrew Bible is my word. I am cosmos. As for wine sellers—why suddenly this attack on wine selling, a very ancient trade?

JESUS: I ate and drank—drank wine—with publicans and sinners. I made wine to bless a feast. I drank wine at my last supper and gave it to the world as a sacrament.

GOD: The only temperance is from within, and if there be temperate men there must be the intemperate also. From whence do you come?

BRYAN: I am just from the Scopes trial, Dayton, Tennessee, Earth.

INGERSOLL: Ha, now we shall get it direct. What was the purpose of that law called "the monkey law"?

BRYAN: It was to defend religion, to defend the Bible, to punish the atheists and agnostics who taught differently from God's own revealed word. It was to protect God.

GOD: So I need protection. Who revealed this word of mine? and when and where and how?

BRYAN: Anyone has only to look at a monkey to see man is not descended from a monkey.

DARWIN: O dear! O dear!

INGERSOLL: Do you take the Bible literally?

BRYAN: Of course. The revealed word of God—literally—every word of it. Who dares tamper with God's holy word?

INGERSOLL: So you believe Joshua and the sun; the fiery furnace; the whale and Jonah; Noah and the ark?

BRYAN: Yes, exactly. Yes. I am glad you mentioned Noah. Noah must be here. Lord, can we have Noah as a witness against the infidel?

GOD: Call Noah.

(ST. PETER goes out. Presently a voice is heard.)

NOAH (*Outside*): A life on the O-ocean wave, a home on the ro-rolling deep—hic—Shiver my timbers——

GOD: That is Noah.

(NOAH *comes in.*)

NOAH: Blast my eye—hic—eyes——

GOD: Noah—Noah. Drunk again.

NOAH: No, your Nip-nipotence. Just happy, 'eavenly 'appy. Splicin' main—main brace.

GOD: Well, Noah. These friends want to hear about that voyage of yours.

NOAH: Wich—wich voyage? Had s'many voy—voyages.

GOD: He's told about his many wonderful voyages till he believes them. The great voyage, Noah, with the Ark and the animals.

NOAH: Yes. Greatest voyage ever was.

GOD: Now, Darwin here——

NOAH: I know Barnum. He tried to im-mi-tate my-me-hic—menagerie.

GOD: No. Not Barnum—Darwin. He says man is not descended from a monkey, but developed on his own tree.

NOAH: Sure. His own tree. Every monkey on his own tree. Man descended from a monkey? What fool says that? Didn't I have all the people there was on earth in my ark? Eh? Did I or did I not? Me and my family was all the people there was on earth. And didn't I have all the monkeys too? Eh? Then how'n hell——

GOD: He's a sailor. Go on, Noah.

NOAH: How'n hell were we in the ark descended from the monkeys in the ark? Makes me sick—not seasick—never was seasick. Just sick. Man's descended from me—me—women too. Everybody's descended from me. Am I a monkey? Show me the scurvy land-lubber that says I'm a monk-monkey.

BRYAN: God be praised. Here is a witness.

GOD: Tell about the voyage, Noah. Did you save all the animals of the world?

NOAH: That's what I done—did. I saved 'em all—all. Elephants, graffes—giraffes, lions, tigers, leopards, rabbits, deer, horses, cows, donkeys, polar bears, grizzly bears, lots of bears, kangaroos, buffalo, sheep, goats, wolves, foxes, arctic foxes, jackals, wart-hogs, hip-hip——

INGERSOLL: Hooray.

NOAH: Hip-hip-po-pot-amuses-potamuses, rats, cats, lice, fleas, mice, mosquitoes, all the bugs, toads, snakes—I hate snakes. O everything, everything that couldn't swim. And we rigged a ladder on the starboard quarter for seal, walruses, otter, beaver, muskrats and so on, to climb out onto a raft.

GOD: Did you save everything that is now on earth, Noah?

NOAH: Yes sir. Every—everything—every damn thing—and a lot of fishes too.

ST. PETER: Fish?

NOAH: Yes, fish. You ain't the only one knows about fish. I say *fish*. Says I to myself, says I, there is going to be so much fresh water poured down, the sea won't even be brackish, so I laid—laid in a hundred and twenty barrels of salt—and after the rain poured for forty aays—my log showed forty-one, but I won't contradict the Bible——

BRYAN: Blessed be God.

NOAH: Eh? Poured for forty days, nights, too, and the whole earth was covered with fresh water. The mackerel and cod and such used to come ev-every day to the ship's side for their ration of salt—salt.

BRYAN: God is wonderful. There is proof for the agnostics.

NOAH: That's what makes them so salt now. You have—have to soak them.

BRYAN: The agnostics?

NOAH: No, you lubber. The codfish and mackerel. Well, things went on all right after all the people was drowned-ed—drowned dead, but we was tired of voyaging and nowhere to go, and we wanted to feel the earth under our feet, and one day we was going under slow bell, sou-sou-west by sou, bound for nowhere, mother was in the galley getting supper, and I see a spike of land off the port bow, and just then Ham—he's my son—Ham was on watch as lookout—he sings out "Land ho, off the port bow."

BRYAN: Excuse me. But you sent out a raven and a dove.

NOAH: Did I? Well, I done so many things that voyage.

BRYAN: Yes, and the dove brought back an olive branch.

NOAH: Funny old bird.

BRYAN: And then you sent out a raven.

NOAH: See here, who's telling this story? Did you keep the log or me? Was you skipper or—or me?

GOD: He's Bryan.

NOAH: I don't care if he is. He ain't any brineyier than I am——

GOD: Go on, Noah. Go on. Never mind the brine. You are the world's old salt.

NOAH: Where was I?

GOD: You had just sighted Mt. Ararat.

NOAH: Not yet. I didn't know it was Mt. Ar-
Ar-a—What did you say it was?

GOD: Ararat.

NOAH: I didn't know it was what you said till I
got there. Well, Ham was lookout on the foksle head,
and I seen we was slipping into an awful strong tide-
way, so I sings out to Ham "When I give the word, you
fling overboard the starboard main bower," and he yells
something back, and I says: "None of your back slack;
if I am your father—you fling the anchor overboard
when I give the order." And he hollers back again
something, and I says: "Any more of your insub-sub-
bor-din-a-tion, you young lubber, and I'll put you
in the lazareet in double irons. There won't be no
mutiny on this craft while Noah M. M. is master—if I
am your father." That's what I said. Bust me for a
barnacle if I didn't. And then we was abreast and almost aboard the peak of land, and I sings out "Let go
the anchor. Let her go," but Ham never done a thing,
just commenced yelling again. I seen it was mutiny; I
picked up a handspike and started for him, yelling
"Throw that anchor overboard." So Ham picks up the
anchor and throws it into the sea. "There," says I, "you
young lubber, you might have done that before. Now
take a turn around the windlass and snub her up."
"Snub up, nothing," says he. That's what he says. "If
you wouldn't anchor so close to the wine cask you'd
a-heard me tell you three times that there wasn't any
line on that anchor." That's what Ham said to me—
and me his father; I cursed him so he turned black,
black as coal. It never come off neither.

BRYAN: God moves in a mysterious way.

NOAH: You bet he does. But he don't move no
mysteriouser than I do. He attempting to tell me what

I should drink on a cruise like that, and me his father, as far as I know. But this was no time for family discussion. I had to think quick. We was driftin' past. I called Satan—Satan was the elephant—and threw two half hitches of two-inch rope around his tail, made that line fast to a hawser and shoved him overboard, with Abel, the giraffe, on top of his back, and a loop of rope around his neck running to the same hawser. I wasn't taking no chances. It was one of the most pearl-pearlous situations I was ever in—in all my eggs-experience as snavigator—deep water sailor.

GOD:  Go on, Noah.

NOAH:  You never seen—saw such a fight as Satan put up against that tide-rip. The water boiled all over him. I was pretty anxious as grub was gettin' low, and wine lower, but my heart fell back to position when I saw him throw his trunk around the peak and at the same time Abel slipped off his back, and with his long legs galloped around the mountain top with the hawser, and we warped the good ship Ark inshore with the windlass and made fast. That's the way the world was saved and all the animals in it. I'm awful dry.

BRYAN:  Have some water.

NOAH:  Water! Water! If you had had the experience with water I've had you wouldn't mention it to me slong si live.

BRYAN:  Water is God's work.

NOAH:  So is wine and scarcer.

BRYAN:  May I ask the patriarch a question?

GOD:  Certainly.

NOAH:  What did he call me?

GOD:  It's all right, Noah.

NOAH:  I don't want—want any of these fresh— fresh prentices callin' me out of my right name——

GOD: It's all right, Noah—Go on, William.

BRYAN: I would like to know if you ever found the anchor.

NOAH: We certainly did. When the water sub-subside—when the water went down, we found it hangin' on a point o' rocks. It's now in the Funny-Funny-men-Funny-mentalist Museum, University of Tenny-Tennessee.

BRYAN: Wonderful! I must let the brethren know that. That will confound the scoffers. One more question: You referred to yourself as "Noah M. M." What does "M. M." signify?

NOAH: Master Mariner.

BRYAN: This has been a most wonderful revelation, and that we may put to shame the scoffers, will you tell me just one thing more. How did you feed the animals?

NOAH: Easy, Easy. Hay for the grass eaters—baled hay and seaweed, and when the cold storage meat for the flesh eaters ran out, we fed them new-born kids or lambs, rabbits, guinea pigs, things like that—like that, and when the female hip-hip-po-pot-hip-popot-amuss had a young son, we killed the father. He lasted a long time. The cats caught fish and the birds ate worms.

BRYAN: Worms. What worms?

NOAH: O there is always worms in sailors' grub.

BRYAN: Praise God.

NOAH: No, they don't.

GOD: Thank you, Noah. I always enjoy your yarn. It is never twice alike. You may go. But remember, the juice of the grape is better the more moderately it is taken. Try to get the real good of it.

NOAH: O Lord. I got the habit on that voyage. I

was crazy for the feel of the land. I think I ought to be allowed something for saving the world.

GOD: In moderation, Noah. Moderation is joy.

(NOAH *goes out.*)

DARWIN: He is a real old sailor—not many left.

GOD: I love my men of the sea.

DARWIN: Omniscience, how about the secret of the creation of life?

GOD: Charles, would you create by a great principle and universal law, which of itself works toward infinity, or by fussing each time with a lot of separate experiments? Am I less a scientist than you?

DARWIN: I understand, Omnipotent.

(*All go out except* GOD *and* JESUS.)

GOD: Well, my son, what do you think now of your earth brethren?

JESUS: Father, why are you so pessimistic about man?

GOD: Why? Because he does not understand freedom. He is afraid of it. He hasn't the backbone to stand up and take the consequences.

JESUS: By your own great law he has struggled upward. If there are Bryans there are also Darwins.

GOD: How many?

JESUS: If only one, is there not hope?

GOD: Perhaps. It all rests in their desire, their intelligence, and the life of the sun.

JESUS: Give me my million years for man.

GOD: He needs them.

## XLI
## GOD'S IN HIS HEAVEN—
## ALL'S WRONG WITH THE WORLD

(*God on the judgment throne. Below and around, a crowd of angels and souls.* ST. PETER *comes in.*)

ST. PETER: Omnipotence, two souls wish to speak to you.

GOD: Let them.

ST. PETER: Come.

(SACCO *and* VANZETTI *come forward and stand before the throne.*)

GOD: Yes, Bartolomeo—Yes, Nicola. But were you not at the seat of Justice on earth—at Boston, Massachusetts, before a Judge? And Judges, you know, are in my image. They hold life and death in their hands. They are without passion or prejudice. They temper justice with mercy. Was there not a prosecuting attorney? Prosecuting attorneys are attorneys for no man, but for the State, which also is in my image, seeking no man's blood; giving to the accused the benefit of every doubt. Prosecuting attorneys swear to fullfil the sacred duty of protecting those on trial against passion, prejudice and falsities. Seeking only the truth. They are attorneys for the accused as well as for the State and will conceal nothing.

INGERSOLL: They do that in England.

VANZETTI: But, good gentlemen, in our case Frederick G. Katzmann, the prosecuting attorney, concealed everything in our favor and twisted the truth to falsity —and educated witnesses to lie that we might be killed.

WM. LLOYD GARRISON: In Massachusetts? Impossible.

GOD: O quite impossible, in Massachusetts.

DANIEL WEBSTER: "Massachusetts, there she stands——"

VANZETTI: Listen. Captain Proctor, an arms expert, was asked at our trial if he had an opinion whether the "mortal" bullet came from Sacco's pistol, and he said "yes"—that in his opinion it was consistent with it.

INGERSOLL: Curious answer! Seems carefully worded.

VANZETTI: Yes. Listen. He made an affidavit after the trial (never contradicted) that his answer was agreed on in this peculiar form between him and Katzmann and Katzmann's associate, Williams, because he found no evidence that the bullet was from Sacco's pistol and he did not believe that the bullet came through Sacco's pistol, but in his opinion it might have come from *any* Colt automatic, so Katzmann, Williams and he agreed on an answer that really meant the bullet might have come from any Colt automatic but was framed to lead the jury to believe it came from Sacco's Colt automatic.

INGERSOLL: He conspired with Katzmann and Williams to deceive the court and jury?

VANZETTI: Well——

INGERSOLL: "Massachusetts, there she stands."

VANZETTI: The Judge charged the jury that the effect of Captain Proctor's testimony was that in his opinion the bullet which killed Berardelli was from Sacco's pistol—though Captain Proctor had just the opposite opinion.

INGERSOLL: And these men, who are Attorneys for the accused as well as for the State, that "seeks no man's blood," let that go?

VANZETTI: They framed it to go that way——

MARK TWAIN: "Massachusetts—There she stands."

INGERSOLL: As a headsman. New trials have been ordered for less than that—as in People v. Montesanto, 236 New York——

VANZETTI: But when we asked for a new trial, Judge Thayer changed completely from what he had said when instructing the jury and now said Captain Proctor did not testify that the bullet passed through Sacco's pistol but only that it was *consistent* with it.

INGERSOLL: Why didn't he make that quibble plain to the jury, or, not having made it plain to that jury, why didn't he give a new trial before another jury and give these men a fair chance for their lives?

VANZETTI: Oh, Judge Webster Thayer asked to be assigned to try us. We were radicals.

INGERSOLL: A judge who asks to be assigned to the trial of a cause is not unprejudiced. He has a motive. One way or the other he has a motive and is prejudiced.

VANZETTI: He was delirious with patriotism and hatred of "Reds." We were "Reds."

INGERSOLL: Like that other disgrace to the judicial ermine—Kickshaw Landis, the baseball judge.

VANZETTI: We were then in the very midst of the Reign of Terror——

MARK TWAIN: Started by that other disgrace, Mitchell Palmer, the Quaking Fighter, Attorney General of the United States for Ego Wilson.

GOD: I know, I know. A wild raid against innocent men because of their political beliefs, and because they were aliens. Hate, Hate, Ignorance and Fear, turning bankers, newspapermen and politicians into ravenous beasts. I know all that. Pass on.

VANZETTI: Sacco and I were "Reds"—we were for a better social order, but not by force.

TOM PAINE: No anarchist can believe in force or he is not an anarchist.

VANZETTI: We worked steadily at our jobs, every day, he in the shoe factory, I pushing my fish cart.

RABELAIS: Ah, ha!—Where is Peter? He should look into this. A fellow fisherman in trouble.

ST. PETER: The Church has a representative in Boston.

VANZETTI: The Cardinal. Yes. He served tea but refused to lift a finger for reds and heretics. We had literature in our possession teaching pacifist and anarchist doctrine, and we were frightened with Mr. Palmer and his men. Our friend Salsedo was seized in New York. He was held incommunicado for days. Then his body was found on the pavement under the window of the room where he had been held. We did not know what to expect. That is why we carried arms. That is the cause of every act of ours which Judge Thayer called "Consciousness of Guilt." He and the prosecutors had three grounds of identifying us with the crime. First, eye witnesses—and that broke down; even the judge said that. Second, the bullet thought to have been from Sacco's pistol—and that broke down, but unfortunately, only after the verdict, and when the conspiracy to mislead the jury by Captain Proctor's fixed-up answer had done its work. And, lastly, this "Consciousness of Guilt," which could mean anything you wanted it to—it all depended on the patriotic frame of mind. So all through, Judge Thayer, Governor Fuller and the Lowell Committee stuck to "Consciousness of Guilt."

God, what evidence could we have brought which would have convinced such men of our innocence?

GOD: None. (*To* GABRIEL.) Call the Recording Angel. Tell him to bring the Book of Infamy. (GABRIEL *goes out.*) Go on.

SACCO: I had my pistol a long time. From when I was a watchman in the shoe factory. Bartolomeo also a long time. He peddled fish and often late at night had as much as a hundred dollars with him——

MARK TWAIN: Packing a gun is nothing in the United States. I used to carry two but never could hit the stump I used for a man. I can't get over the fact that a witness who would have said that the fatal bullet did *not*, in his opinion, come from Sacco's pistol, but could have come from any Colt automatic, was, by the prosecutor's conspiracy, made by weasel words to imply the opposite, and that the judge was himself fooled by it and so charged the jury, yet afterwards said it amounted to nothing and refused a new trial. If that is the fair unbiased judge in the likeness of God——

GOD: I deny the likeness, Samuel. Ah, here is the Book of Infamy! Hold it ready. Go on, Bartolomeo——

VANZETTI: In this environment of delirium with hatred of foreigners in the very air—with a terrible vague fear of Anarchists, Socialists, Communists, any who challenged the perfection of the present social order—we were tried.

INGERSOLL: Easy to see the outcome—the Chicago Anarchist case over again.

MARK TWAIN: The breaking waves of hate dashed high on a stern and hidebound coast.

VANZETTI: Judge Thayer knew we were "Reds." He and the prosecutors knew the Federal sleuths had been after us—to deport us.  The United States detectives consulted with Mr. Katzmann to "get" us.  To burn us in the chair was better than deportation.

TOM PAINE: It·seems to me Judge Thayer, Governor Fuller and the Lowell Committee had the same idea.

WM. LLOYD GARRISON: Fuller?  Fuller, the politician—Alvan T. Fuller—who as Representative in Congress hysterically shrieked from the floor for the lawless deportation and destruction of all "Reds"?  Fuller!  O, my God.

(*The Recording Angel lifts his pen.*)

GOD (*To the Recording Angel*): Not yet.  Go on, Barto!

VANZETTI: The very opening words of Judge Thayer to those summoned to serve as jurors began with an address on the brave boys who had dared death in France in the performance of duty—and called on these *venire* men to show, on their part, the same patriotism, the same courage and devotion to duty—ending with "There is one thought which I would like to burn into the fibre of every citizen throughout this land, which is that he who is willing to accept the blessings of this government should be perfectly willing to assume his share of its duties and responsibilities."  The Judge knew we were Reds, knew that we had been Pacifists and had refused to serve in the war because we believed it a wicked, capitalistic war.  He knew all this had nothing to do with whether or not we had killed Paymaster Parmenter and his clerk, Berardelli, but——

INGERSOLL: Ah, ha!  I have it.  Eureka!  That's why he asked to be assigned to try you—Jeffries over again. He should wear a hangman's cap.

VANZETTI: And afterward, the first words of his charge to the jury were "Although you knew that such service (jury duty) would be arduous, painful and tiresome, yet you, like the true soldier, responded to that call in the spirit of supreme American Loyalty. There is no better word in the English language than loyalty."

GOD: That depends on what you are loyal to. I may be the supreme stupidity, the extreme of wicked ness. What is the name of this——

MARK TWAIN: Ass.

GOD: This Judge. Don't insult a wise and patient beast, Samuel.

VANZETTI: Judge Webster Thayer. You can guess for yourselves what our chance was—we "Reds"— Pacifists—Draft evaders—refusing to fight in what we thought a sordid, capitalistic, imperialistic war—when the first and last words of the judge to the jury were as I have said.

INGERSOLL: Omnipotence! If you only knew the weight of a judge with the jury. If you only knew how little evidence counts againt prejudice and emotion and the views of the judge! Ah, you are smiling! Forgive me for instructing, Omniscience! Of course you know!

GOD: My son might instruct you, Robert, on the fairness of trials when the Ruling Order calls for blood.

JESUS: Was there evidence against me? Was I guilty? Only as these are guilty. Guilty of trying to make a better world, where there is no war.

GOD: Go on, Barto!

VANZETTI: The very first question put to me by Mr. Katzmann on cross-examination was, "So you left Plymouth, Mr. Vanzetti, in May, 1917, to dodge the draft, did you?"—"When this country was at war you ran away, so you would not have to fight as a soldier?"

I had to say "yes," and from that time on, the jury was against me.

INGERSOLL: Why, that was fatal. The war hysteria was still on and the Quaking Fighter was shrieking against "Reds" and aliens. But what on earth had this to do with the murder for which these men were on trial? Nothing.

LINCOLN: Much. It meant conviction through passion and prejudice—not through evidence.

INGERSOLL: "Massachusetts. There she stands——"

MARK TWAIN: In her soiled underclothes.

(*Recording Angel lifts his pen.*)

GOD (*To the Recording Angel*): Not yet. Go on.

SACCO: It was the same with me. Mr. Katzmann asked me "Did you say yesterday you loved a free country?" And, God, I did love a truly free country—that's what we came to America for. Barto and I thought we were coming to a free country. Then Mr. Katzmann said "Did you love this country in May, 1917?" It was hard to explain—I didn't speak much English—and he wouldn't let me explain, but kept hammering that I would not fight for the country. By this time, in the very beginning, the jury hated us. It was good to get rid of us. It was loyalty. Judge Thayer approved this kind of questioning.

VANZETTI: The Lowell Committee did not condemn this.

MARK TWAIN: "Massachusetts. There she stands——" winking at Infamy and beckoning him to her that they may have bastards.

SACCO: What do you think, good, just God, how they identified me as a murderer? Mary Splaine and Frances Devlin heard shots and looked out of their third-story factory window and saw a car sixty or eighty feet away at high speed and saw it for maybe two seconds at most.  And on first examination before trial they could not be sure, though we were shown to them without others to confuse them, but in the trial they swore positively.  They had been educated by the prosecuting attorney.

INGERSOLL:  Dr. Morton Prince of Harvard College, psychologist, said such observation, in so short a time, under such excitement, was humanly impossible.

SACCO:  But we found a man after the trial—Gould—who was right at the car, and was shot at—a bullet through his coat—and he said we were not in the car.

INGERSOLL:  Eternal Justice.  Couldn't you get a new trial on that?

VANZETTI:  No.  In denying the motion for a new trial, Judge Thayer said Gould's testimony was of no value—merely cumulative—and said our verdicts did not rest on the testimony of identification but on consciousness of guilt.  We thought not he, but another jury, should pass on these new facts.

INGERSOLL:  And the Lowell Committee followed this idea?  That the testimony of a man watching the whole affair—close up—and shot at—was not important enough for another jury to pass on?

VANZETTI:  Yes.

MARK TWAIN:  "Massachusetts—There she stands!" She has even dropped her underclothes.

VANZETTI:  Both Gould and Burke, who would have also said we were not in the car, told all this to the prosecution, but were told to go—that their testimony was of no value.

INGERSOLL:  Is this fair?  Is this seeking the truth? Is this concealing nothing—or is it seeking to convict in spite of truth?  O, Webster Thayer——

DANIEL WEBSTER: Don't call that man "Webster." The dead have some rights.

VANZETTI: The Lowell Committee especially approved this.

INGERSOLL: "Massachusetts! There she stands——"

MARK TWAIN: She shows her sores.

SACCO: I had a true alibi. My mother died, and my father was alone. I had some money in the bank and I wanted to go to my father.

INGERSOLL: Wait a minute. You had money in the bank?

SACCO: Yes; fifteen hundred. Savings for a long time. I worked in shoe factory a long time. I ask my boss if I can be off April fifteenth—that is the murder day.

INGERSOLL: Wait a minute. A steady workman with money in the bank doesn't join a murder gang.

SACCO: No. And I have wife and children. I want to go to my old father in Italy—and I like to get a passport so I ask my boss if I can be off April fifteenth, the murder day. The first time I am off in two years. I take up a big photograph of me to the Consul's office, and everybody laugh that I should bring such a big photograph. The Consul's clerk remember this and swore I was there that day. Then I met in Boston Mr. Bosco, editor of *La Notizia*, and Professor Guadagni. They talked to me about a dinner to be given Mr. Williams that day. They testified to the jury they were sure of the date because of this dinner.

INGERSOLL: Wait a minute. A. L. Lowell, President of Harvard University, when these gentlemen were before his committee, said that their evidence would be most important "*if true.*"

LINCOLN: It certainly would be. It would clear

Sacco. He couldn't be murdering in South Braintree and getting a passport in Boston at the same time.

INGERSOLL: President Lowell told Messrs. Bosco and Guadagni it would be most important, *if true*, but that they were mistaken—that the Williams dinner was April the thirteenth. These two gentlemen insisted they could not be mistaken. There was only one Williams dinner and it was on April fifteenth. The President of Harvard lost his temper. Why lose his temper? Wasn't he seeking truth? Was he a partisan? He told these gentlemen in heated language—why heat?—not much veiled—in effect that they were deliberate liars. They went off. Hunted up a newspaper that reported the dinner as April fifteenth. They took this to President Lowell, who apologized to them for his heated language and asked them to say nothing about it to the newspapermen. Why not? He did not mention it in the report of the committee.

LINCOLN: But Robert—It must occur to you, as it does to me, that if this testimony was very important— as it certainly was—acquitting Sacco, "IF true"—why was it no longer important when proved true?

INGERSOLL: Ask Lowell.

LINCOLN: I'll tell you!—Everything from first to last, no matter how worthless as evidence, was evidently good to Judge Thayer and Governor Fuller, and to the Lowell Committee, if it convicted these men and relieved Massachusetts of them. And nothing was to be believed if it acquitted them. No,—not a revelation from this Throne.

INGERSOLL: "Massachusetts! There she stands——"

MARK TWAIN: Calling dogs to lick her sores.

VANZETTI: True. Nothing for us would have been believed even if coming from Heaven. I had no need to murder.  My people in Italy are well off.  People of good standing.  I worked every day.  So did Sacco.  He asked just one day off in two years.  Do workingmen making good wages stop off just one day for a planned murder with a regular band of professional murderers?  All the police say the job was by professionals.  If we were in the gang,—why only one day off from honest work in years?  Where is the money we got?  Not one cent has been traced to us.  Why did we go on after the murder in our steady work just the same?  Only, as it so happened, trying to hide our literature.  I, too, showed my alibi.  Men and women, good women, housekeepers who had bought fish from me that day.  No,— nothing was believed.  Where did my fish rot while I was away murdering?  But someone murdered Mr. Parmenter and Mr. Berardelli.  The police at once suspected the Morelli gang of professional bandits, who made robbing freight cars and shoe factories their business.  All the State's witnesses agreed the driver of the murder car was blond, thin, very white, sickly.  They agreed there were five or six in the car.  If we were there, where are our partners?  The United States experts said the robbery was done by professionals.  But Sacco had been at work every day but the fifteenth.  I had pushed my cart every day.  No one called us professional criminals.

SACCO:  The Lowell Committee said it was not by professionals.

MARK TWAIN:  Well, they ought to be good judges of professional crime.

VANZETTI:  Then after our trial, Madeiros, one of the Morelli gang, under sentence of death for a later bank robbery and murder, confessed that the murder was done by the Morelli gang, and that he was in the car.  He

said he couldn't stand seeing Rosina Sacco coming to
see her husband with the kids, and he knowing Nicola
was innocent. He tried in jail many times to speak
with Sacco, but Nicola was afraid of him as a stool-
pigeon. Then he wrote. Not that he had a hand in
the killing, but that he was in the car. I would not
think much of that if he were surely to die any way,
but his case was on appeal. He had much hope. But
our lawyers only took his confession as a tip to run down
the Morelli gang. After Madeiros' tip, everything came
from outside discovery. The band were Joe Morelli,
and his brothers, Mike, Patsy, Butsy and Fred. Also
Bibba Barone, Gyp the Blood, Mancini and Steve the
Pole. Bibba Barone and Fred Morelli were in jail at
the time of the murder. Joe and several others were
under five indictments for stealing shoes from the Slater
and Morill factory, but were out on bail. Joe was afterwards sent up for this. It was the Slater-Morill pay-
roll that was taken by the murderer. The gang was evidently familiar with the Slater and Morill premises and
pay day. The murder car was a Buick. Joe Morelli
owned at this time a Buick that the police say never
could be found after the murder. At the trial all the
testimony was that the driver of the murder car was
thin, pale, sickly—a blond. Steve the Pole, according
to Madeiros, drove the car. And everybody knew that
Steve the Pole was a thin, pale and sickly-looking blond.
The fatal bullet came from a 32 Colt Automatic. Joe
Morelli carried at this time a 32 Colt Automatic.
They never could fix on us the five other bullets found
in the bodies, but Mancini carried a pistol of calibre and
type to which the five other bullets found in the bodies
fitted. When he was sent up for robbery, Joe Morelli
made an arrangement with a fellow prisoner that if

ever he needed it, this friend would give him an alibi as in New York City, on April 15, 1920. But he did not need it. When we "Reds" were arrested the Morelli gang was dropped. No one knows where they are. No one cares. They were not "Reds." They were not Anarchists or Socialists or Communists. They were not agitators. They were perfectly satisfied with the government and the conditions.

MARK TWAIN: Why not? Most thieves are. So are Thayer and Fuller and Lowell and Stratton and Grant. Dreamers working for a better day for the workers of the world do not suddenly become bandits for one day and go murdering for money.

VANZETTI: And where is the money? Madeiros after the robbery, banked $2,800 and went to Mexico. In planning his later crime, also a murder, he told his partner Weeks how the Braintree robbery was done. Weeks had nothing to fear. He was not under sentence of death, but only for a term of years. These things do not come from Madeiros, only the start—that the Morelli gang did it. All the rest is from the outside—much from the police—and from records.

INGERSOLL: As once a lawyer I cannot stand this. Surely Judge Thayer felt here was matter which another jury should have a chance to consider, as well as the Gould testimony.

VANZETTI: No, not testimony. He never testified, but made affidavit when we asked for a new trial.

INGERSOLL: Gould was the man shot at by one of the bandits?

VANZETTI: Yes, and it was his opinion that the fatal bullet was not from Sacco's pistol. Like everything in our favor—Judge Thayer said it amounted to nothing —was only cumulative.

INGERSOLL: And Governor Fuller and the Lowell Committee followed suit.

MARK TWAIN: Good dogs! Good, yellow curs following their master!

LINCOLN: Ah. But their master .was not Judge Thayer. Their master was their class. The Ruling Class. Which was howling for blood. Remember that the ruling class that knew none of the facts but only that these men were "Reds," was howling for their blood.

VANZETTI: Governor Fuller's statement and the Lowell Committee report are both so full of misstatements of record facts that either they did not read the record carefully or distorted it.

INGERSOLL: The judge is all. How could there be a fair and impartial trial with a judge of patriotic hysteria? Hating these men as "Reds" and Pacifists. Determined to be rid of them.

MARK TWAIN: His opinion of sixty pages denying the motion for a new trial convinced the *Boston Herald* (which at first was against one) that from facts he himself recited, Sacco and Vanzetti should have a new trial. And it printed the famous editorial "We Submit," which reviewed the points of the Judge's decision one by one. It said the Judge's opinion "carried the tone of an advocate rather than an arbitrator." It received the Pulitzer Prize as the big editorial of the year.

VANZETTI: Judge Thayer spoke to Mr. Loring Coes at the Golf Club, calling us, "Those bastard anarchists down there." He said to him that parlor Bolsheviks could not intimidate him and get us off, but he would show them, and "get" us, and he would like to hang a few dozen of the radicals. Mr. George U. Crocker, a prominent Boston lawyer, made affidavit that Judge

Thayer had often cornered him at the Club to vent his spleen against our first attorney, Mr. Moore, and would read the decisions he intended to make against us, saying, "I think that will hold the 'Long-haired Anarchists.' " And frequently he said "Wait till they get my charge!" Mr. Frank P. Sibley, dean of the Boston newspaper reporters, made affidavit that Judge Thayer embarrassed the reporters by discussing the case and showing his hate and prejudice, saying on several occasions, "Wait till they hear my charge!" Mr. Beffel, another reporter, said the same, and that the Judge added "that will get them!" The affidavit of Mrs. Lois B. Rantoul, "Observer" at the time for the Federated Churches, says the Judge was buttonholing outsiders to convince them of our guilt and twice endeavored to make her believe us guilty.

MARK TWAIN: O, wise and upright Judge! How I do honor thee!

VANZETTI: There is much more of this. None of it contradicted. The Lowell Committee found it true.

INGERSOLL: They did, did they?

VANZETTI: Yes, and said he had been indiscreet and guilty of a violation of judicial decorum. But it did not follow that he was not impartial and fair—*on the Bench.*

INGERSOLL: And those men—Judge, Governor, Committee—are Massachusetts.

MARK TWAIN: "Massachusetts! There she stands!" The poor old whore!

LINCOLN: Have they no consciences?

GOD: Their consciences are the approval of their own class.

MARK TWAIN: So were the consciences of the witch burners. "Indiscreet"! "Decorum"! The Morelli gang were indescreet to murder Parmenter and Berardelli—it certainly was a breach of decorum——

(*Enter a Soul.*)

SOUL: I am one of those witches murdered at Salem, Massachusetts, by fear—ignorance—hate——

(*Enter Roger Williams.*)

ROGER WILLIAMS: Though I taught universal love, the doctrine of the "Friends," I was obliged to flee from the bigotry and hate of ·Puritan Massachusetts.

WM. LLOYD GARRISON: I was threatened with death and my press was wrecked in Boston by fear—bigotry—ignorance—because I held there could be no property in human flesh and blood.

INGERSOLL: "Massachusetts!   There she stands!" Massachusetts of the Blue Laws—Massachusetts—fountain of every narrow, intolerant, persecuting bigotry that has cursed this puritan polluted land.

GOD: I know.  Go on, Barto.

VANZETTI: In sentencing us to be burned to death by electricity the Judge was careful to say he did not do this—the Jury did it.  The Law did it.  But who pushed the Jury as putty?  Who made the law of the case?  Who refused us new trial though the power was absolutely his?  Who said he would "get us"?—"Wait till they hear my charge"?  Judge Webster Thayer—and Judge Thayer said to Professor L. P. Richardson of Dartmouth College, who so wrote to Governor Fuller: "Did you see what *I* did to those Anarchist bastards?" What *I* did.  And this when the book was closed and we were certain to die.

JESUS: O, Father, did the man have no thought of the agony he brought to them—to the wife—the children—the old father?  You, Father, have infinite understanding—but this man had neither understanding nor pity,—and justice without pity is of hell.

(*Satan enters.*)

GOD: Just in time, my friend. I wish to call your attention to Earth, which you and Jesus value so much. In a town called Boston is a man named Thayer— Webster Thayer—a judge——

SATAN: Don't mention him.

GOD: I present him to you—on Earth and here-after——

SATAN: Why do you belittle me? I thought we had arrived at a better understanding.

GOD: You refuse?

SATAN: Am I a dog that fleas should be put upon me?

GOD: Then you refuse?

SATAN: Absolutely, Omniscience. I am not an as-sassin. This man would be contemptible in hell. Let him drift through eternity alone.

GOD: Take up the Book of Infamy.

(*The Recording Angel lifts the book and his pen.*) Write in imperishable black:

### WEBSTER THAYER

Leave him alone forever on that page. To Time I leave the names of Alvan T. Fuller, A. L. Lowell, S. W. Stratton, Robert Grant.

(*A terrible hissing is heard as from a den of serpents.*)

Leave them to Time. (*The hissing ceases.*) Bartolomeo —Nicola—look at me—NOT GUILTY!

(*A great flashing of wings. Heaven trembles with song. "Hosanna"—"Hallelujah." Souls and angels go out—leaving God upon his throne, with Jesus by his side.*) Man! Man!

JESUS: Patience, Father. He will learn mercy. He will learn love.

GOD: Let us go to one of the unpeopled stars and be alone a while.

(*They go out.*)